SPUTNIK
INTO SPACE

SPUTNIK
INTO SPACE

by M. VASSILIEV

With an Introduction and Notes
by WILLIAM BELLER,
co-author of *Satellite*

THE DIAL PRESS   1958   NEW YORK

Library of Congress Catalog Card Number: 58-11429

Originally published by the State Publishing House,
Moscow
under the title of
ПУТЕШЕСТВИЯ В КОСМОС

© 1958 by Souvenir Press Ltd., London
American edition © 1958 by The Dial Press, Inc.

Translated by Mervyn Savill from the Italian
"Su Sputnik Nel Cosmo"

First English language edition published in 1958 by
Souvenir Press, Ltd.

DESIGNED BY WILLIAM R. MEINHARDT
PRINTED IN THE UNITED STATES OF AMERICA
BY THE HADDON CRAFTSMEN, SCRANTON, PENNA.

Contents

INTRODUCTION

THIS is the first book about artificial satellites to come out of the Soviet Union. It was written for the Russian layman to tell him the meaning of space flight. This the author does simply and well, and for this reason, *Sputnik into Space* is highly recommended. But for discerning readers, this book does much more than explain space flight—it also explains something about the Russians.

It is clear that *Sputnik into Space* was not meant to be read outside the Soviet. How else are we to explain the author's occasional lapses into domestic fantasy such as his blithe statement that "a heavier than air flying machine"—built by A. Mojaisky—"had risen from the ground in 1882?" However, later on he repents and says, "Barely half a century has passed since the flight of the first aeroplane." This gives the credit for pioneering airplane flight back to the Wright brothers.

There is no doubt that *Sputnik into Space* was a best

seller in the Soviet Union. The book's first edition minus Sputnik material was published by the State Publishing House, Moscow, in 1955. Then the work was called *Traveler into Space*. A member of the Soviet Academy of Sciences collaborated and was scientific editor. This fact was sufficient to guarantee the book's authority and public acceptance. To understand why, one must realize that membership in the Academy is one of the highest honors that can come to a Russian scientist. He is part of an elite group that formulates and directs the country's vast scientific effort.

A further note on the book's value is that V. V. Dobronravov is the Academy member involved. In 1954, the president of the Academy, Alexander A. Nesmeyanov, said, "Science has reached a stage when the sending of a space ship to the moon and the creation of an artificial satellite of the earth are entirely feasible operations." He appointed a Rocket Technology Committee to deal with these problems and also those of interplanetary flight. Heading the Interplanetary Navigation Subcommittee was V. V. Dobronravov, doctor of physico-mathematical sciences. Shortly, the problems of interplanetary flight were transferred to a newly formed Committee on Astronautics, headed by the distinguished physicist L. I. Sedov. Dobronravov soon began playing an important role in this committee, which directed the work on the Sputniks.

From the book's style, we can surmise that M. Vassiliev is a journalist. He is probably young because this is his first book. That he was enormously encouraged by its success we can judge by his having completed three more books in the year following publication of this one. After Sputnik II was successfully launched, Vassiliev again col-

laborated with Dobronravov to revise *Traveler into
Space,* which became the present volume.

What may strike the reader as odd is the author's
neglect of the three recognized pioneers in modern rocket
development and theory, Robert Goddard, Hermann
Oberth and Eugene Sänger. These omissions would not
have been so apparent had he not dealt at length with
a minor figure such as Nikolai Kibaltchitch, who is best
known for having tossed the bomb that killed Czar
Alexander II. Still, the reader will probably be more
amused than surprised when he sees just how big some
of the Russian blind spots can get.

In a book of this type we have the rare chance to learn
something about the Soviet's space program. The author
quotes his collaborator as saying that the stage after
Sputniks is to build manned rockets, then inhabited
satellites, and finally a space ship that will reach the
moon. The date Dobronravov sets for man orbiting
around our natural satellite is 1980.

That Dobronravov's estimate is realistic is confirmed
by the American Rocket Society. In a report sent to the
President of the United States in October, 1957, the
Society wrote that the United States has the capability
of putting a man around the moon within fifteen years,
and having manned two-way flights to the moon, including landings, within twenty years.

What Dobronravov's time table means is that the Soviet
Union seriously intends reaching the moon by 1980. The
Russians seldom bluff about technical matters. We saw
this first when they said they were working on a hydrogen
bomb, and then they exploded one. We saw this again
when they said they had an intercontinental ballistic mis-
sile, and then they launched one. And we saw it a third

time when a committee of Russian scientists wrote in the
Evening Moscow in April, 1955, that they would put a
satellite in orbit early in the International Geophysical
Year, and they did. Their announcement was made three
and a half months before President Eisenhower made a
similar one on behalf of the United States.

Perhaps *Sputnik into Space* is more than a primer of
space travel. It may even contain the record of Soviet
things to come.

William Beller

Washington, D.C.
March 19, 1958

SPUTNIK
INTO SPACE

Chapter One

DESTINATION MOON

LAST moments of farewell . . . The photographers and newsreel men are taking their last shots and using up their last reels of film. Th gigantic space ship in the centre of the cosmodrome is ready for launching. Its tanks are full of the most efficient propellant; the receiving sets and the mechanism of the automatic control have been given a final check. But the hatches are still open and the lightweight aluminum ladders have not yet been drawn up. The crowds are still on the field.

But now only a few moments remain before zero hour. The crowd is already dispersing the photographers and newsreel men have already put their cameras back in their cases. The hatches are closed. Now the control tower is in radio communication with the crew.

In the cabin of the ship last preparations are being made. The crew are lying on soft pneumatic hammocks to reduce the effect of gravity on their bodies. All eyes

are fixed on the clock with the huge second hand on the
dial. Now only two turns remain . . . 2 minutes to go
. . . 30 seconds, 10 . . . 5 . . . The hand reaches the
vertical. . . .

A mighty roar, the ship vibrates and the shuddering in
its body warns the passengers in their hammocks. Then
they feel as though their limbs had turned to lead. They
can hardly open their eyes or pass their tongues over
their parched lips.

How slowly the hand of the clock seems to advance!
It has not even made half a turn since the motors started
to fire. They will continue to fire for 110 seconds—almost 2 minutes—to give the ship circular velocity of 6.8
miles per second.[1] Perhaps the clock has slowed down as
a result of the gravitational pull. . . .

The captain of the space ship calls the ground control.
"Everything in order," he reports. The crew is stand-
ing up well to the "over weight." In actual fact during
relaxation before the flight all the members of the crew
had been subjected to a far higher g; finally to 450 ft.
per second. Now the overweight corresponds only to 330
ft. per second, i.e., about 10g.[2]

The second hand has now completed its second tour.
The vibration suddenly ceases and an unearthly silence
reigns. The ship is already 400 miles above the earth.
The prescribed speed has been reached and the motors

[1] "to give the ship circular velocity of 6.8 miles per second." Author probably means escape velocity. Circular velocity at sea level
is 4.91 miles per second.

[2] Throughout the text, the author gives "g" and accelerations in
units of velocity (feet per second) instead of in acceleration units
(feet per second per second). See also, "acceleration so many feet
per second," p. 2.

cut off. Now the hammocks can be slung and the port curtains opened.

Who piloted the ship during this time? Who switched on and cut off the motors, regulated their firing to ensure that acceleration did not exceed the permissible, constantly diminishing the flow of propellant and progressively releasing the boosters?

Automatic controls have piloted the ship. Before launching the captain merely stabilized the speed of acceleration to reach the required orbital speed. These robots carried out all the other necessary operations. Some of them are installed in the ship itself; others are on the ground. The orders are transmitted to the ship by radio.

An important item is the acceleration regulator. This consists of a weight fixed to a spring. Upon its tension depends the flow of propellant injected into the combustion chamber. Should the tension exceed a certain figure the flow ceases and, vice versa, if the tension falls too low the flow increases.

The speed of the ship is determined from the ground. Radar operators attentively follow the progress of the ship. Its invisible beams contact the ship, are reflected and return to earth. They can calculate the exact position of the ship by the time taken by the signals to reach it and return to earth, while its speed can be calculated by the distance between two consecutive beams.

At the moment of launching, when the bodies of the crew grew leaden-weighted from the gravitational pull, they could only follow the progress of flight on the instruments controlled by their companions on the ground.

As soon as the space ship reached a great distance from

the earth and radar echo began to grow faint, another apparatus starts to function; it receives the signals from the Earth and will transmit them immediately after duly magnifying them. Thus in any event the principle of determining the speed and acceleration of the ship remains unchanged. In this way, too, the control on the ground is given greater radius of action; according to certain calculations this could be extended as far as a landing on Mars.

Instruments, therefore, have carried out all these maneuvres quite automatically. In front of the screen in the control room below, the operator on duty and the instruments give the results of the readings in clear: speed, acceleration so many feet per second,[3] amount of propellant burnt, temperature of the nozle etc., etc.

The counterparts of these instruments are to be found in the ship. But here they are not encumbered with the complicated machinery for working out the measurements and calculations; the data obtained are radioed to the ship from control.

The need to avoid any extra weight is only one of the reasons why part of the instruments remained below. There is another equally important reason.

We have already spoken of the solar system and how insignificant are the dimensions of the planets with respect to the enormous distances that separate them. To "aim at" the tiny speck of dust—the planet Mars with a diameter of only 4,300 miles—at a distance of 34 million miles is as difficult as firing a shot from Constantinople to hit the eye of a sparrow on the roof of a church in Berlin as, according to Baron Munchausen, one of his servants did. Space ships, at least at first,

[3] See footnote 2.

would prefer longer journeys which require less energy and the trajectory to Mars would be not 34 million miles but 5 times more. Moreover, a rocket in motion has to join a planet which is also in motion. It is, so to speak, aiming at a moving target.

What precision all the calculations of the various stages of ascent, flight and landing demand! An error of only one second on a bearing, or a few feet per minute in speed would make the rocket pass hundreds of miles away from the planet for which it was making.

Automatic instruments alone are capable of such precision.

The captain in the space ship and the operator on the earth merely watch the instruments and follow out orders given to them in advance.

Naturally there will be a great many of these during a long voyage. A stray asteroid whose influence has not been foreseen may be its attraction make the ship deviate from its course and this must be corrected by means of the auxiliary jet motors. Possibly the trajectory must be determined in the last stages when any faults in the calculations will become apparent. All this is the hands of the captain of the space ship and the operator on earth who have attentively followed the progress of the flight.

The landing will in all probability also be entrusted to automatic instruments.

. . . Our ship is approaching the Moon. Through the huge windows of plastic material we can see quite clearly its grey seas—probably lakes of solid lava-mysterious pockmarks and craters, bright rays which issue from the craters spreading hundreds of miles over the moon's surface. Soon the landing will take place on our satellite. In the meantime the ship is not making direct for the moon; it is not flying but falling laterally towards it. The motors must now be switched on. Otherwise as a result of the moon's attraction the ship would crash onto its surface like a huge meteor and the force of its explosion would probably form a new crater.

The captain presses a button and four tenuous wires, the radio aerials, emerge from the nose of the ship. In profile it looks like an enormous fish cast up from the sea bottom of some far distant planet. These aerials will pick up signals transmitted from the earth. The direct beams from Earth to Moon will accomplish the space ship's movements—its nose is now pointed away from the moon with the sensitive aerials and the motors reversed.

The moon's surface approaches ever more rapidly. Now the serrated mountain ranges can easily be distinguished. The ports are covered with metal shields and the crew retires to the hammocks.

Once more, as at the moment of landing, the ship vibrates and the roar of the jet motors can be heard. This time, too, the captain did not switch them on; the automatic instruments did it for him. The radar beams from Earth contacted the space ship's aerials and passing them touched the surface of the Moon. Their reflections were also recorded in the ship. As soon as the interval between the reception of the beams from the earth and their reflection from the moon showed that the time had come to start braking, the motors were automatically switched on.

The fiery breath of the jets has sucked up a fine layer of dust from the surface of the Moon. The dust rose like a cloud only to subside immediately. The messenger from the Earth, the first space ship touches down gently on a flat basalt surface, seared by a flaming hurricane of gas.

And there is the moon outside the ports. The mountain chain resembles the spine of a monstrous dragon, black with impenetrable shadows and glistening with crystals . . .

Landing on the moon will be the first great step taken by man into the unknown. Let us now examine the path he has already traversed on his quest for knowledge . . .

Chapter Two

THE UNIVERSE IN WHICH WE LIVE

MAN has a very clear notion of the place our planet occupies in the universe.

Our Earth is one of the planets of a solar system at the centre of which is the incandescent Sun. The temperature of the sun's surface reaches 6,000° and its mass is 333,432 times greater than that of the earth. Let us try and get some idea of this system. Let us represent the earth as a tiny circle with a diameter of 1/10″. We shall find that no sheet of paper exists large enough to represent the sun on the same scale. Nor will a table or the area of a normal room suffice. We should have to place the sun at a distance of 60 yards from the earth and depict it with a circle having a diameter of more than 18″.

Within this gigantic circumference would be included the orbits of the two planets which lie between the earth and the sun—Mercury and Venus. To portray the former we should have to draw a circle of less than 1/25″ at a

distance of 23 yards from the circle representing the sun
—this would be Mercury. Next we should have to draw
a second circle 43 yards from sun to represent Venus.

To record on our plan the entire solar system and to
include the orbit of the outermost known planet, Pluto,
we should need more than the area of a large stadium.
We should have to place the circle representing this
planet at a mile and a half from the centre of the system. This outermost circle would be the limit of our
solar system as we know it today, and our plan would
now cover an area of 14 square miles.

Try and distinguish from the back seats of a stadium
if a threepenny bit is placed in the middle of the
arena. Naturally this would be an impossibility. It would
be equally impossible, even if we were suspended at
sufficient height above our plan, to distinguish a single
circle of it in view of the insignificance of the circles
compared with the area covered by their orbits.

If we now wish to enlarge our plan and use the same
scale to include the position of the stars nearest to our
sun, the whole area covered by Europe and Asia would
not suffice. The nearest star in space is, in actual fact,
a modest starlet, visible only in the Southern Hemisphere, appositely called Proxima. Proxima Centauri is
4.3 light years away from us. This means that its rays of
light, which travel at 186,283 miles per second, take just
over 4 years to reach us.

Let us now reduce our plan a million times so that
the orbit of Pluto now corresponds to the 1/10″ circle
with which we represented the earth. Naturally on this
plan we should be unable to see the circles of the
planets, even under the most powerful microscope. The
sun would be represented by a dot the size of the frac-

tion of a micron. Only in this way could we perhaps succeed in plotting the position of the nearest star. Yes, we could do it, but we would need a sheet of paper several miles square; even on this scale, Proxima would be placed 20 miles away from the solar system.

Such is the scale of interstellar space: the Sun represented by a speck of dust visible only under a microscope and a score or so of miles away another speck of dust denoting another sun. And these are our nearest neighbors. And not neighbors in space but in the stellar system.

Our astronomers have today ascertained that our sun is a member of the colossal solar system consisting of about 15,000 million stars known as a galaxy. The stars of our particular Galaxy are visible on clear nights; a fainter mass of stars forms the Milky Way which meanders across the sky like a white riband. It entirely surrounds our planet and thus we are not on the fringe of our stellar city.

The dimensions of this city are gigantic. If we attempted to trace its confines on our plan we should fail: the diameter of our city is approximately 85,000 light years and our sun is about 23,000 light years from its centre. The sun and the host of countless stars revolves about the centre of the galaxy at a speed of about 66,000 m.p.h. It completes a single revolution in approximately 180 million years. Once more the whole area of Europe would not suffice to contain, at this reduced scale, the region that man has already embraced with the power of his intellect.

Nor are these the limits of our knowledge of the infinite universe. Astronomers have discovered in its black depths an enormous number of galaxies similar to our own. They have succeeded in measuring the distance with results that surpass the imagination. Light takes thousands and millions of years to reach us from these neighboring stellar systems.

What conclusions are we to draw? Should the Universe we have discovered overwhelm our imagination and our reason by its immensity, boundlessness and grandeur?

By no means! On the contrary, the majestic picture of what we have already conceived affirms the limitless possibilities of human thought and convinces us that every natural phenomenon is capable of solution.

A bare 300 years ago, Galileo was the first to scrutinize the sky through his telescope. He could scarcely have discerned a general view of the nearest "environs" of our earth. Today an audacious attempt is already being planned to explore those "environs." It is perhaps pointless to state that the conquest of the nearest planets will not be the ultimate step taken by man along this path. And shall we not perhaps today regard all the stars as Galileo, 300 years ago, regarded the planets?

Zeta in Auriga is the name of a rather faint star in the constellation of Auriga, one of the more modest constellations visible in the night sky. This is what we know today about this particular star:

Zeta in Auriga is a double star, a system of two suns rotating about a common center of gravity. One of the pair gives out a reddish orange and the other a bright white light.

The orange star has a vast diameter compared with our sun, since it is 294 times larger. But its mass is only 20 times greater than that of the sun. This means that the density of its matter is lower than that of the sun. Actually it represents .000001 of the density of water,

compared with the sun's density of 141. Its surface
temperature is about half that of the sun: 3100°. The
white star is ten times greater in mass than our sun and
125 times greater in volume. Its density is also far greater
than that of its orange companion, although it is 48
times smaller.

The data on the composition of the orange stars atmosphere already compiled by scientists are very interesting: its total circumference is enormous—about 28
million miles. The upper strata of this colossal gaseous
capsule consist of rarefied hydrogen and calcium gases;
in the lower, denser strata is to be found a considerable
quantity of metallic gases, including iron. The orange
giant rotates on its own axis and completes one rotation in 785 days. A ray of light takes 980 years to cover
the distance between Zeta in Auriga and the Earth.
Naturally no man has ever approached this star, for man
has not yet left his own planet. All the information we
have gleaned about this double star has been pieced together from a faint ray of light which has been on its
way for some thousands of years, not to forget that it
arrived refracted by the earth's atmosphere.

The Beginning of a New Era

Perhaps among scientists who deal with exact science
astronomers are the only ones who cannot subject at
will the object of their investigations to the direct action
of this or that factor.

Actually a technologist who does not attempt to subject the object of his researches to this or that reaction

In this case the shell will describe a trajectory flatter than the surface of the globe and will begin to fly away from the earth. At this juncture, as a result of the earth's attraction its speed will diminish and eventually it will begin to fall earthwards: but now it will be describing not a circle but an ellipse. The shell will travel round the earth exactly as the earth travels round the sun—following an elliptical path one of its foci being our planet.

If we increase the muzzle velocity of the shell still further the ellipse will be still more elongated. This ellipse can be elongated until the projectile reaches or passes the moon.

But unless its initial speed has exceeded 8.25 miles per second it will remain an earth satellite.[1]

A projectile which at the moment of firing is given a velocity exceeding 8.25 miles per second will leave the earth on a parabolic trajectory. Whereas an ellipse is a curve whose ends meet, the ends of a parabola never meet. Moving along a parabola we should never return to our point of departure: both its extremities are directed towards infinity.

But even leaving the earth at this speed the projectile could not yet fly towards infinity. The powerful attraction of the sun would deform its trajectory, would close it upon itself like the trajectory of a planet. It would become a tiny independent planet in the family of planets of our solar system.

[1] 6.9 miles per second, not 8.25 miles per second, is escape velocity at sea level, and the value decreases with altitude as the pull of gravity becomes less. Any velocity greater than 6.9 miles per second would be that of escape.

The velocity of about 5 miles per second (this velocity depends on the height of the mountain from which our gun is fired) is called circular velocity; from 8.25 miles per second elliptical; 8.25 parabolic and beyond this speed, hyperbolic.[2]

To direct our projectile beyond the confines of the solar system, to overcome solar attraction it would need to be given a speed exceeding 10.5 miles per second.[3]

Here it must be noted that the values we have given to these velocities are valid only on earth. If we lived on Mars, circular velocity could be reached with far greater ease: there it is represented by only 2.5 miles per second while the parabolic only just exceeds 3.25 m.p.s. On the other hand, to despatch a projectile on a space journey from Jupiter would be more difficult than from the Earth; the circular velocity of that planet being 26.45 m.p.s. and the parabolic 38.25 m.p.s.

By Cannon to the Moon

Therefore to leave on a space flight it is necessary to give the space ship at least circular velocity. But naturally the problem is very much more complicated. The elementary calculations we have adopted do not take into

[2] Actually, 4.91 miles per second is circular velocity at sea level. But a satellite orbiting in the atmosphere would soon be burned up. At 167 miles altitude, circular velocity is 4.83 miles per second, and escape velocity is 6.84 miles per second. Roughly then, between 4.9 miles per second and 6.9 miles per second we can have elliptical orbits, and if the speed reaches 6.9 miles per second, we have escape.

[3] To escape from the solar system we need 19.8 miles per second, not 10.5 as the author states. (Ref. "General Characteristics of Satellite Vehicles," Norman V. Petersen, The Journal of Astronautics, Summer 1955.)

account the resistance of the atmosphere, which is very considerable in the case of high speed flights.

How can a space ship be given such a vast speed? "Fire it from a cannon" was the first answer. Jules Verne despatched the characters of his novel to the moon in this way. But the great adventure story writer made a grave mistake—a mistake which many others in his day and later repeated. Accurate calculations have shown the impossibility of giving a projectile escape velocity by firing it from a gun using any known explosives (except those of an atomic nature).

Let us imagine that we have exploded a highly explosive substance in a vacuum, transforming it instantaneously from its solid to a gaseous state of the same volume. This gas, which would initially have a very high temperature and pressure, would start to expand violently and its particles would disperse in all directions. Meeting no obstacle, they would move at the maximum velocity allowed by their inherent energy. But this velocity would be far below that of space requirements. It would not exceed 2 miles per second.

If the explosion were to take place in the breach of a cannon having only one exit for the gas, its speed could not exceed this figure. This would result because a part of the gas being unable to leave the rear portion of the cannon would remain immobile and its energy would be transferred, so to speak, to those particles which had freedom of movement. But in this case, too, the particles of the gas which would form on the explosion would be unable to develop orbital speed.

Even less would a projectile set in motion by a flow of gas in expansion be able to do this. Calculations have shown that even in a case where the projectile weighs considerably less than the powder charge, with the longest barrel, it is impossible to give it a speed exceeding 3-4 miles per second.

It is true that in recent years scientists have discovered a new method of concentrating the energy of such explosions: the so called phenomenon of cumulatory effect. This phenomenon can be observed from the following experiment:

Take a glass of water and a syringe and let a drop fall from a height of 8-10 inches onto the surface of the water in the glass. The drop will touch the water and merge with it; on the surface a slight concavity will be formed. This hollow will start to level out and a tiny drop will be projected into the air from its centre. Now watch what happens after the cavity has fired its drop into the air; hardly has the fallen drop formed the cavity than from all sides the water rushes in to fill it up. These currents meet in the center and all their energy is concentrated on the tiny drop which has spurted into the air.

This so called cumulative effect is exploited in modern artillery. The currents of gas which have formed at the moment of combustion in such projectiles make for the center and one of them acquires a colossal velocity (several miles per second) and a colossal destructive power. In 1946, the Soviet scientist Pokrowsky by this method imparted to the flow of a metal in gaseous state a velocity of 15 miles per second.

Place the space ship at the center of a huge cumulative charge and it might conceivably be given orbital velocity. But indubitably at the moment of meeting of the explosive currents of gas, the space ship, however

able to give our space ship escape velocity. But if it were built 900 ft. long as in Jules Verne's novel, the acceleration undergone by the ship on leaving the barrel would crush the passengers to pulps.

To decrease acceleration it is necessary to extend it over a longer time. We should therefore have to lengthen the barrel of our solenoid gun.

By how many times?

If we accept that in certain conditions man can, without ill effects, stand an acceleration of about 10g, we should need a barrel of . . . 500 miles. Obviously it would be impossible to build such a gun.

But perhaps one day a means will be found of using cannon firing magnetic projectiles for the purpose of launching supply material into space and for the transport of pay loads. Today we must exclude from the methods we can employ to embark upon space travel both the gun charged with powder and the electric gun.

The Space Sling

Attach a stone to a stout cord. Let it revolve and release the stone. Together with the cord it will fly in a certain direction by the effect of centrifugal force.

Naturally it is impossible to hurl a stone by this method into space. The number of rotations we can give to the stone by swinging it with our arm is far too small. But centrifugal force can assume very great proportions. In technicology cases have been known when it has caused the smashing of heavy vanes secured to the rotators of steam turbines etc. In such cases the fragments of the destroyed parts acquired a very great velocity. Could not centrifugal force then be utilized in space travel? Why not attach the space ship to the periphery of an immense disc and then let it go? No, this is not possible.

The blades of a steam turbine which are capable of 3,000 m.p.m. are usually made of the best quality steel. These blades are generally three times more flexible at the extremities than at the shaft so that their solidity may be uniform: the stress placed on the metal as the result of centrifugal force is thus evenly distributed. The peripheral velocity of turbine blades rarely exceeds 1,000–1,300 feet per second.

If we wished to construct a blade of uniform solidity, the periphery of which would have escape velocity, giving it a thickness of 1 millimeter, the center would have to be seevral miles thick; thus it is impossible to use centrifugal force for this end.

Other plans for using centrifugal force to reach escape velocity exist. One suggestion was to build a ringed tunnel and to launch inside it a nacelle—the space projectile. This would entail a series of revolutions with a continual increase of velocity. At the end of the rings the tunnel is built straight and the projectile car is launched into space. Calcultions, however, have shown that this plan is fundamentally unsound.

The nacelle revolving in the ringed tunnel would be subject to enormous centrifugal force. This force would not differ as regards the passengers from the force of acceleration obtained by firing a gun. It would pulverize, smash and denigrate their bodies.

But in order that the "overweight" should not exceed the admissible limits, even by reducing it to 130 ft. per second a ringed tunnel with a diameter of more than

2,000 miles would be required. This instrument of space travel could hardly be contained in the whole of Russian territory in Europe. Nor would it be feasible to construct such an edifice vertically.

Is it impossible, then, for man to reach outer space? Will he remain eternally a prisoner of the earth, forced to judge the nature of the other worlds from theories deduced from weak rays of reflected light, blurred photographs and dim spectra? Will man never set foot on the rust red soil of Mars or on the pale moon?

Chapter Three

THE GLORIOUS UNDERTAKING

ON the 1st March, 1881, a magnificent carriage drove along the Neva Prospect in St. Petersburg. A figure suddenly loomed up in front of it; a swift gesture—and a bomb was hurled into the carriage. The roar of an explosion, police whistles, a second explosion and it was all over . . . On the orders of the executive committee of the "Will of the People" Party, Alexander II, Emperor of Russia had been assassinated.

The bomb had been made by Nikolai Kibaltchitch, an ex-student of the St. Petersburg Academy of Medicine. On the 17th March he was arrested and imprisoned in the fortress of Peter and Paul.

Not a strip of sky could be seen through the narrow frosted glass iron-barred window of the prisoner's narrow cell. A huge sheet of ice descended from the sill to the floor, transforming the cell into a veritable ice-box. The walls were covered with damp stains which made eccentric patterns. For some time this was the home of the young revolutionary.

Condemned to death and awaiting execution, the boy did not bother his head for one moment about his surroundings or about his approaching death. He worked furiously, preparing his precious gift to the human race: the design of a new flying machine. A machine that would allow man to fly to the stars.[1]

It was the prototype of a rocket place with a motor driven by gas expelled from a nozzle. "Let us imagine," wrote Kibaltchitch, "a cast iron cylinder . . . hermetically sealed except for a test opening breech block at the base . . . Place in this cylinder a quantity of compressed powder of cylindrical shape and light it from below; from the combustion will be produced gases which will exercise equally balanced pressure on the entire inner surface of the cylinder. The gas pressure alone at the breech will not be balanced and will have an outlet downwards through a hole in the platform. If the cylinder be inverted and given a certain pressure of gas . . . it should rise into the air."

As will be seen from this, Kibaltchitch, the scientifically minded revolutionary—he was not yet 27—had grasped the principle of rocket action, not presupposing as many of his colleagues did, even later, that it moved by repelling the air through the flow of burning gas. His machine would have flown equally well in a vacuum. The principle upon which it worked is the only possible one known today that will allow man to realize his age old ambition—space travel.

We cannot fail to be moved by the letter written by

[1] Kibaltchitch wrote a paper called, "Preliminary Design of a Rocket Airplane," but it is doubtful that he saw the craft being used for space travel. (Ref. *Rockets, Missiles and Space Travel,* Willy Ley, The Viking Press, 1957, p. 91.)

this youth: "In prison and a few days before my death, I have committed this plan to paper . . . If my ideas are found to be practical, I shall be happy to have rendered an immense service to my country and to the human race . . ."

A few days later this boy, who might have become a brilliant scientist, was executed. His plan together with his letter and his precious donation to the world remained in the archives of the Czarist Secret Police and did not come to light until after the 1917 Revolution.

Independent of Kibaltchitch and with no knowledge of his plan, Konstantin Ziolkowsky put forward the same idea of using rocket motors for space travel.

A list of Ziolkowsky's published and unpublished works amount to about 100 titles. They deal with geology, cosmogony, aerodynamics and astronautics. In 1895, studying the problems of the flow of gas on solid bodies of various shapes, he built the first Russian aerodynamic tube. At the same period appeared his plan for an aeroplane. We must recall that until then a single heavier than air flying machine—built by A. Mojaisky—had risen from the ground in 1882, but the details of this flight were not known to Ziolkowsky at the time.[2] The most important part of Ziolkowsky's scientific legacy is his work on astronautics. As a boy he began to think of space travel. The idea of using the jet principle came to him about 1883. The scientist drew a rapid sketch: a manned balloon suspended in space. To give it directional movement the men in the balloon are firing can-

[2] It seems odd that the well-informed astronaut K. E. Ziolkowsky did not know of A. Mojaisky's flight.
See Chap. 6, "The Exploration of The Ionosphere" (p. 60) for apparent contradiction.

non shells in the opposite direction. The force of the recoil propelled the balloon.

This was only a rough draft but, in 1903, Ziolkowsky published a scientific paper, "The Exploration of Space by Means of Reaction," in which he propounded the idea that rockets could be developed for use in space travel.

The propeller blade which rises whistling into the air, from a bobbin rotated by a cord, from this childish toy, the prototype of the modern aeroplane and the helicopter, was known at an early date to Mojaisky and to the Wright brothers, the inventors of the aeroplane. For more than a century, however, men had believed that the future of flight lay not in these toys but in balloons and airships. It was a glorious achievement on the part of the pioneers of aviation to get into the air their first kite-like aeroplanes which in less than 30 years completely supplanted the clumsy flying machines of the 18th and 19th centuries.

The firework rocket has been in existence for many thousands of years. It has been used not only for pleasure and for signalling but also to case lines to ships in peril and in wartime. But no one before Kibaltchitch and Ziolkowsky[3] had seen in this toy which burst in a rain of bright stars in the night sky the powerful motor which would carry man from earth into space.

[3] Ziolkowsky, sometimes spelled Tsiolkovskii, was the first man to treat the rocket as a scientific propulsion means that could be used for space travel. However, because his works were in Russian and for a long time untranslated, they were not known to the American rocket pioneer Robert Goddard nor to the German, Hermann Oberth, who reached similar conclusions independently.

Rather than Kibaltchitch, the Russian pioneer I. V. Meshcherskii should be mentioned for his late 19th century work on the dynamics of bodies of variable mass.

These two Russian scientists must be given full credit for this.

Kibaltchitch died at the age of 27. Ziolkowsky was fortunate enough to be able to continue his work after the October Revolution. He had time to elaborate his theories of rocket flight, to compile mathematical analyses of its movements, and to indicate a series of important points towards the solution of the general problem—the conquest of space.

As early as 1903, Kiolkowsky proposed for space travel the replacement of the primitive powder-charged rocket by the liquid propellant jet motor. Here is a description of this motor given by the inventor:

"Let us imagine a projectile of the following type: an elongated metal chamber containing a large quantity of substances which when mixed will immediately cause a powerful explosion. These substances exploding with sufficient regularity and uniformity in the prescribed space, will escape in the form of hot gas along tubes enlarged at the ends in the manner of funnels or wind instruments . . . The mixture of the explosive substances reaches the narrow end of the tube: here concentrated, burning gas collects. They will emerge from the funnel aperture at the enlarged end with an enormous relative speed. It is clear that in certain conditions such a projectile will rise into the air like a rocket . . ."

Why in his plan did Ziolkowsky discard solid propellant in favour of liquid? Because all known explosive substances—even the most powerful—produce less energy per lb. than ordinary combustible liquid. Thus 1 lb. of the most powerful explosive known today, nitroglycerine, produces at the moment of explosion only 512 lb.

—calories. On the other hand, 1 lb. of ordinary petrol (excluding the oxygen which takes part in the reaction) produces at full combustion, 2,000 grand calories. Liquid combustile produces energy gradually as it burns, while in the case of nitroglycerine it is released almost instantaneously on the explosion. But it is precisely this instantaneous release which damages the rocket. Ziolkowsky stresses that the combustible in his rocket explodes "with sufficient regularity and uniformity."

It is true that holes can be picked in our comparison; nitroglycerine needs no oxygen in order to explode, whereas petrol must have oxygen to bring about the explosion. But even an adequate mixture of petrol and oxygen (in this case the petrol represents the carburant and the oxygen the combustible element, although the mixture is generally termed combustible) can only produce 1,030 calories—1½ times more than a lb. of nitroglycerine.[4]

Naturally Ziolkowsky did not intend to use crude naphtha in his rocket. He intended to fill the rocket tanks with hydrogen and oxygen instead of liquid. United in a given proportion these will produce the detonating gas—the hottest and most combustible known to Ziolkowsky. In the combustion of hydrogen in oxygen more than 1,200 calories are produced per lb. of fuel burnt.

What is the conclusion? If the basic principle has been defined, if the motor capable of functioning in space has been found, if the perfect design of the space

---

[4] The petrol represents the fuel or combustible element while the oxygen is the oxidizer. The word "carburant" is not included in either Websters or The Oxford dictionaries.

ship exists, why has a practical and suitable construction not appeared?

The Relation of the Masses

Ziolkowsky deduced the formula of rocket propulsion. The analyses of this formula show that the rocket in space can develop an unlimited velocity. But in order to do this it must consume an enormous quantity of propellant.

Let us try and elucidate this problem.

The space ship is about to take off from the cosmodrome. It is gigantic and very weighty. With a howl and an infernal din great columns of fire spurt from the exhausts in its stern; they are incandescent gases which travel at a speed far exceeding that of a hurricane. On these fiery columns, as on stilts the vessel rises from the field at an increasing rate of acceleration. Now the "stilts" have left the ground and the space ship is airborne, leaving behind it a trail of fire. After a few minutes it will have reached the limits of the atmosphere; it will have developed escape velocity and the motor will be switched off. The space ship will accomplish the greater part of its voyage towards the nearest planet on the force of inertia, although it will be influenced by the forces of attraction of the Sun, the Earth and the planets.

It is obvious that at the moment of leaving the earth, the ship will weigh far more than once the jet motors have completed their task. In the interval a large quantity of propellant has been consumed and the energy released has imparted escape velocity to the space ship.

The mathematician will term our space ship "a body of variable quantity."

The speed of the ship naturally depends upon the quantity of propellant consumed and the speed of the emission of gas from the nozzles.

The greater the speed of the burning gases, the greater the speed developed by the rocket, (equal to the amount of propellant burnt).

Theoretically, using hydrogen and oxygen in liquid state as a propellant it would be possible to achieve a velocity of 12,000 ft. per second.

Scientists of all fields have combined to solve this problem. Analytical chemists have selected the propellant and evolved methods of rationalizing the combustion; heat specialists have designed the shape of the combustion chambers and nozzles; metallurgists have experimented with fire-resisting metals (the lack of these at present hampers the work on increasing the speed of the flaming jets), and the designers have worked out efficient motor cooling systems.

In addition to the speed of the gas flow and the amount of propellant consumed, the final speed of the rocket on leaving the earth also depends on the intensity of the combustion of this propellant and upon the time the jet motor is in action. It is easy to conceive that the whole of the propellant could be burnt leisurely, little by little; the gases would then be expelled in a steady jet from the nozzle at a calculated speed—and the ship would remain earthbound. The power developed by such slow action of the motor would be insufficient to overcome the force of gravity.

The more precipitous the rate of combustion, the more powerful the motor, the greater the acceleration and the less propellant consumed in order to achieve the necessary speed.

But we must remember that the human body can only stand a certain rate of acceleration, and the lower this is kept the better.

The designer hovers between Scylla and Charybdis. He would prefer to increase the velocity of the jet expulsion but this would cause a rise in temperature in the combustion chambers, resulting in a considerable shortening of the motor's life. He would prefer to design a space ship with a modest rate of acceleration to avoid endangering the health of the crew, but in this case he would have to increase the amount of propellant carried.

He studies his calculation tables. Here are the details of one of these tables compiled on the basis that heat is obtained by injecting a certain quantity of hydrogen into the combustion chambers.

If the temperature in the combustion chamber is 2,700°, the expulsion speed can, in theory reach 21,500 ft. per second; if the temperature is raised to 5,700° the expulsion speed will be 36,900 ft. per second.

The worried designer lays aside his table and picks up another. Onec more he studies the inexorable columns of figures.

If, given a gas expulsion speed of 6,800 ft. per second, we wish to give the space ship escape velocity but without exceeding an acceleration of 1.1g (about 36 ft. per second to the second) for every lb. of weight we shall have to burn 57,200 lbs. in order to achieve the required speed.

This is naturally impossible. The designer decides to worsen the living conditions of the crew by subjecting them to a faster acceleration. Let us say to 10g (about 330 ft. per second to the second). It will not be easy for a man to stand this acceleration, but the designer will do his best to make the crew's work easier in these conditions. He will build special hammocks in which they will recline during these moments of "over weight" so that the weight will be evenly distributed over their entire bodies. Secondly the time during which they will be subjected to overweight will decrease with respect to the first alternative. It is difficult to determine which the human frame will better stand: a moderate overweight of long duration or a powerful one of short duration.

The designer begins to look round for possibilities of increasing the speed of the gas expulsion. To do this he has to raise the temperature in the combustion chambers and to find new types of propellant developing more calories. This will entail an intense cooling of those parts of the motor which come in contact with the hot gases, above all the combustion chamber and the nozzles. If he were to make them porous and force the liquid propellant through the pores? By evaporating on the surface of the parts in question it will absorb a great quantity of the heat and act as a coolant. The designer therefore decides to increase the gas expulsion speed to 16,250 ft. per second. The table in front of him gives him the following information:

Given a gas expulsion speed of 16,250 ft. per second and the admissible acceleration speed of 10g to reach escape velocity 25 lbs. of propellant will be consumed for every lb. of weight of the rocket.

The relation of the masses gives a similar result to a metal bucket filled with water. It is possible to compile a table showing a reciprocal relation of weights—it will be a barrel with thin walls of wood filled with fuel, but not a gram will remain over for the weight of the motor, the passengers or the scientific instruments. On the other hand, not all the propellant must be consumed on take off because some will be needed for landing on another planet and for the return journey to earth. This is an indispensable load.

What is to be done? The human body will not stand any further increase in overweight so this path definitely is closed. It is difficult to envisage an increase in the gas expulsion speed in the light of existing scientific knowledge. The designer lays aside his tables.

The relation between the mass of the rocket at take off (a rocket with a full load of fuel) and a rocket which has already achieved escape velocity rules out all possibility of designing a space ship. The designer has proved with the cast iron logic of figures that space flight is impossible under the existing state of scientific conditions. Is this true?

Space Trains

Yes, it is true. The designer who first made these calculations was Ziolkowsky. Well, what now? Shall we have to wait for our chemists to find a weighty super-calorific combustible, for our metallurgists to produce metals with super heat-resisting qualities?

No. We must seek solutions to the problem now.

The Soviet engineer Frederik Sander turned his attentions to space flight. According to him, the most difficult part of the journey is the start—the take off and the crossing of the atmosphere. Let us give our rocket wings.

"Wings? Additional weight, therefore."

"The wings can consist of carburant matter," replied Sander, "of aluminum or magnesium. On reaching outer space these wings, which have become useless, can be burnt as fuel in the space ship's motor."

Really! Not such a bad idea to burn the "bucket" as fuel. But this is still not the solution to the problem.

Ziolkowsky had a new idea. He suggested launching into space an entire space train instead of a single rocket. The smallest rocket, designed to explore new worlds, would be carried by a larger rocket which in turn was to be carried as a passenger in an even larger rocket. The number of these stepped rockets was to be determined by the velocity required to be developed.

The rockets would function in inverse succession. Let us imagine a three-stepped rocket about to take off. The motors of the largest rocket go into action first. It shoots precipitously into the sky carrying its two passengers. Its progress can be observed from below through a telescope.

Having exhausted its own fuel, reached a certain height and developed a certain speed, this rocket suddenly becomes detached and abandons its "passengers." This is the moment for the second rocket to go into action; long flaming jets spurt from the nozzles of its jet motors. Burning its own propellant it continues on its way, still increasing the speed.

As soon as this rocket has exhausted its fuel it detaches itself and the third and last motor comes into play. This will be able to develop escape velocity.

Calculations have confirmed the accuracy of Ziolkowsky's idea. During the past few years elaborate plans have been worked out with stepped rockets which would be capable, for example, of reaching the moon. One of these plans envisages the creation of a rocket in ten sections with an initial weight of 63 tons. The launching of such a rocket would enable us to land a weight of 10 lbs. on the moon.

This is of course not a certainty. But is it any more incredible than the first plywood aeroplanes at the beginning of the century which did not even yet know how to fly?

The accuracy and the fruitfulness of Ziolkowsky's idea have found practical confirmation today. Everyone is familiar with the German rocket used at the end of the Second World War—the V2.[5] Developing a maximum speed of about 1 mile per second this rocket launched vertically, reached a height of 115 miles. Another well known rocket, the WAC Corporal developed a maximum speed of .8 miles per second and rose to 43.5 miles.

In 1949 these two rockets were combined. The lighter member, the Corporal, became the passenger of the heavier V2. A contraption was designed to unseat the "rider" from his "mount" when the propellant in the tanks of the V2 were exhausted. Additional mechanisms were installed to start the motors of the smaller rocket at the exact moment it detached itself from its booster. At first sight it would appear that the altitude reached by the smaller rocket should at the utmost be the sum total of the heights attainable by both rockets—in other

[5] The Germans have said more than once that the American Robert Goddard and the German Hermann Oberth laid the groundwork for the V2. In fact, Ziolkowsky's works were not translated out of the Russian until Oberth's had appeared. cf., Ley, p. 104.

words about 156 miles. In reality the WAC Corporal reached a height of 250 miles. This was because the work of the second rocket only began when the combined apparatus was already travelling at a noteworthy increase of altitude on its further flight.

Half Way House

In 1895 Ziolkowsky published a work of science fiction called *Dreams of sky and earth*. This little pamphlet of about 10 pages was eagerly read by secondary school boys who had not yet acquired a knowledge of trigonometry and logarithms as well as by hoary headed scientists who had scaled the peaks of modern knowledge. Written in novel form, it was in actual fact a scientific work. In particular, Ziolkowsky propounded for the first time the idea of an artificial earth satellite.

Today astronauts know that such a satellite will play an important role in interplanetary travel. But what is the nature of an artificial satellite?

When Kepler deduced his laws of the movements of the planets from the Moon. as a result of several thousand observations, he certainly could not suspect that the day would come when man with his own hands would create new planets and launch them on their way according to the laws he had discovered. It is precisely these artificial planets which are a lively topic of conversation today. It is difficult to launch a rocket, even of the stepped type, direct to the Moon, Mars or Venus. It is far easier to launch one to circle the earth as we Russians have already done, by giving it circular velocity.

This rocket, the Sputnik, which today is flying round the world is the first artificial satellite. Let us suppose that instead of carrying the dog Laika it had been large enough to carry men.[6] It would then have become the first human habitation in space. In principle it would not be difficult to establish a regular communication with this first space habitat by guiding unmanned pay-load rockets alongside it. The material of which these rockets would be made could be used to increase the size of the first satellite.

Naturally it will be no cheap matter to despatch tons of cargo from the earth to the artificial satellite. The inhabitants of the satellite would have to limit the list of the materials sent for their personal use. Particularly since in outer space they would not be able to obtain everything in unlimited quantities they needed for life. By means of a collossal greenhouse which would be created on the satellite they would be able to organize complete water oxygen and food systems.

By means of the supply rockets they could build up a store of propellant and piece by piece construct a rocket capable of taking off for the Moon, Mars, and eventually Jupiter and Saturn.

This rocket would not resemble those weighty, massive aerodynamic monsters which reach the satellite from the Earth. The rocket for interplanetary travel launched from the satellite could be of any shape best suited to the requirements of the crew, the propellant and the motors. We must remember that in space there is no gravity and no air resistance.[7]

[6] The dog-carrying satellite was the second.

[7] Our planets and all masses in our solar system are governed by the gravitational field of the sun.

The speed necessary to launch the rocket from the satellite would be infinitely less than that required to launch a similar rocket from the Earth. To travel for example from the Earth to Mars it would be necessary to develop a speed of approximately 8 miles per second, whereas the journey from the satellite to Mars would only demand a speed of about 2 miles per second. The artificial satellite already possesses a space velocity which could be exploited at take off. In this way the satellite is a real half way house on the route to the stars and will go a long way towards the realization of interplanetary travel.

Rocket technique has reached this point today. What are the limitations, and what are the near prospects of realizing the eternal dream of mankind? We shall examine these possibilities in the following chapter.

Chapter Four

THE MOTORS OF SPACE SHIPS

The Battle for Speed

THE engineer designer I. Merkulov, one of the creators of the first static reactor, maintains that the solution to space travel will be the logical development of supersonic aircraft. The gradual increase of speed reached by man has led to the building of aircraft fast enough to travel in the ionosphere, then to the artificial satellite and will lead to the building of a machine capable of flying to the Moon or to Mars.

We can only partially subscribe to this argument. Space flight differs substantially from flight in the atmosphere. The words space flight apply to a machine built by man which leaves the atmosphere under the action of two forces—the force of inertia imparted to the machine by its jet motors and secondly by the atmosphere, like the aeroplane, or subject to air resistance like the rockets. Thus both these types of flight differ from space flight.

We cannot therefore anticipate a gradual transformation from atmospheric to space flight. Their paths of development have at certian moments run parallel and crossed each other, but today they have taken distinctly opposite paths and they will tend to diverge ever more. The genealogical tree of aviation begins with the ideas of Leonardo de Vinci and the models of Lomonossov, via aerodynamic researches of Jukowsky, through turbo and ram jets to supersonic aircraft.

On the other hand, the development of the space ship began with the powder rocket—a familiar toy invented centuries ago by the Chinese—via the work of Ziolkowsky and the modern liquid propellant stepped rockets, which have exceeded the results so far achieved by aviation both in speed and performance. It would appear that these rocket machines are destined to be the forebears of the future space ships. But at the same time, it would be unfair to think that the development of aviation has not favored the technique of high performance rockets. The designers of rockets have not hesitated to call upon a host of interesting technical solutions to be found in aircraft for the building of space ships.

Aviation and astronautics are neighboring fields of science and technology. There was a time when the development of the former prepared the way for the latter: there will come a time when the latter will inform the former of the results obtained and aid its further development.

The development of aviation has been extremely rapid and its triumphs are unparalleled in history. No branch of science or technics has developed with such dash and speed.

In the short span covered by its history, aviation has employed a varied sequence of engines. The pioneers of the aeroplane tried to drive their machines with steam engines. These were soon exchanged for an internal combustion engine which has achieved a high degree of perfection. Within the last decade it has been replaced by the jet. Today researches are being carried out in many countries with a view to using atomic energy in aircraft.

The altitude or the so called "ceiling" of aircraft has also been subject to great changes.

The first aeroplanes flew very low, sometimes not rising more than 30 ft. from the ground. About 1920, the ceiling had been raised to 25,000 ft. Today aircraft have climbed 95,000 ft. and this altitude has been reached by service machines which do not normally fly at these heights.

The story of aviation is largely a story of the battle for speed and altitude.

The first aeroplanes flew at a speed of between 25 and 30 m.p.h. which at the time this was considered very fast. Not until 45 years ago did an aeroplane surpass the 50 m.p.h. mark, while today the speed record stands at over 1,500 m.p.h. This is of course approaching Mach 2.[1] Unrecorded speeds in power dives in the upper atmosphere are considerably in excess of the official figures given. Supersonic speeds of 700-750 m.p.h. have become quite normal for mass-produced aircraft.

The historians of aviation can compile a rising graph of the speed of the aeroplane over the course of the years. The result is not a constant upward line but a zigzag with certain periods of rapid increase followed

[1] 1500 mph is Mach 2.25. Also, on September 27, 1956, the ill-fated Bell X-2 hit 2200 mph, Mach 3.3.

by a horizontal line denoting that no mentionable increase was achieved. The moments of rapid increase co-
incide with some important technical development in
aircraft construction.

Thus the rapid increase in speed which took place
towards the '20s coincided with the change over from
the fabric to the metal wing into which the undercarriage could be raised, greatly diminishing wind resistance. The next rapid leap forward occurred in the second half of the '30s with the introduction of sleeveless
valves. Until then the engine had been forced to breathe
the outside air which becomes increasingly rarefied at
altitude. The engine "suffocated" in the rarefied air and
lost power. For this reason the plane could not take
advantage of the reduced air resistance at altitude.

The introduction of the sleeveless valve gave the
motor the possibility of breathing condensed air when
flying in the upper atmosphere.[2] Now the speed rose at
a bound to 250-300 m.p.h.

But the greatest leap forward occurred about 1945 on
the introduction of the jet engine. The speed increased
to between 350 and 450 m.p.h. The change over from
piston engines to jets was a scientific revolution. This
was the moment when the paths of aviation development
and astronautics intersected, mutually benefiting each
other.

The prime and basic advantage of the jet over the
piston engine consists in the great power developed for
a modest weight. The battle to reduce the specific weight
of aircraft engines—the lowering of the weight of the
engine in respect to the power developed—lasted a very
long time. In 1910, one horse power represented more

[2] It was not the "sleeveless valve" that made a better performing
engine, but rather the advent of the supercharger.

than 5 lbs., in 1950, i.e., within 40 years, it fell to about 1 lb.

The ratio of power of the jet engine is expressed differently and thus there is a certain difficulty in comparing the specific weights of piston engines and jets. Nevertheless, a certain comparison is possible. If we take an ordinary aircraft jet engine running on liquid propellant weighing 375 lbs. developing a thrust of such an engine as equal to 22,000 h.p. But each unit of power of this engine weights only 6 grams—scores of times less than the best piston engine.

The following fact will stress the possibilities afforded by jet engines. Today it is not unusual in aviation to find planes with engines developing a thrust of 10,000 lbs. Given the normal speed for such aircraft as 650 m.p.h. the thrust is equal to the power of a piston engine of 17,300 h.p. Even the best piston engines with a specific weight of only 400 grams per h.p. would have to weigh about 7 tons to develop such power. At the same time the total weight on take off of a fast jet aircraft with the characteristics we have described could be less than 14 tons because the weight of the engines does not exceed 3 tons.

The modern jet aircraft engines differ substantially from those which would drive space ships. Let us see how they would function.

The Motor of a High Speed Aircraft

The liquid propellant rocket motor proposed by Ziolkowsky contains in its tanks as much carburetant as combustible material. It was calculated to function in a vacuum: the solution offered by Ziolkowsky was the only possible one and the only one suitable for this purpose.[3]

But the aeroplane is designed for flight in the atmosphere in which the oxygen captured from the air is sufficient for the combustion of any type of fuel in common use. It is therefore unnecessary to carry the combustible because it can be drawn directly from the air.

The substantial difference between the jet and the rocket motor is that the former takes the oxygen from the air as a combustible while the latter has to carry it.

In the nose of a jet engine is a large circular aperture. When the aircraft is travelling at speed the air enters this aperture. It is sucked immediately into the blades of the compressor which rotate at 14-15000 revs. per minute. The compressor makes the air denser and this compressed air is led to the combustion chamber into which combustible liquid has been injected. On contact with the air it ignites immediately. The temperature in the combustion chamber rises to beyond 1500° and the jet of compressed gas rushes towards the exhausts. But on the way it meets an obstacle: the blades of a gas turbine. The white hot turbine gas thrashes it and makes it rotate. This turbine sets in motion the compressor designed to compress the air which enters the motor. After passing through the turbine the jet of burning gas finds the discharge nozzle.

The nozzle is enlarged at its outer extremity. Passing from a constricted to a broader space the gases expand,

[3] Take "carburant" to mean oxidizer, and "combustible material" to mean fuel. Also, most oxidizer-fuel ratios differ from the figure one. And further, that Ziolkowsky did not offer the only possible solution was demonstrated by the "Explorer" rocket whose last three stages were made of solid fuels.

their temperature and pressure decrease as the speed increases. We already know that the greater the speed of the escaping gas the greater will be the thrust and the more powerful the motor.

The modern jet engine is an engine of high parameters: more than 1500° of heat in the combustion chamber, the speed of the gas jets in the nozzle from hundreds to thousands of feet per second, and 15,000 revolutions per second by the compressor and turbine blades.

At the same time the jet is far more simple than the piston engine and above all more economical in cases where speed is the main requirement. The piston engine will still be preferred for many years for flights at low speeds up to about 475 m.p.h.

Apart from the turbo jet we have just described, three other types exist including the even more simplified ram jet which at high speed (800 m.p.h.) dispenses with a compressor and a turbine: the motor has become a flying spindle. The air compressed by the speed enters the nose while the injection of propellant takes place in the center and the rear part merely consists of an exhaust in the shape of a funnel.

The Hardest Part of the Journey

The reader may ask of what importance are these motors for solving the problems of space travel? They can only function in the atmosphere and to a height of 25-30 miles. Beyond this limit the air becomes too rarefied for sufficient air to be compressed to cause combustion.

But this journey of 25-30 miles through the atmosphere is the most difficult. The major part of a modern rocket's propellant is used up to negotiate this stretch.

A Soviet scientist, N. Varvarov has suggested using the most economical and simple type of turbo jet for this part of the trip.

This is how he imagines the take off of a space ship: an immense craft, equipped with huge wings in which the ram jets are carried and beneath which, in special cabins, are suspended the turbo jets, will be placed at the end of an inclined ramp. The length of this ramp will be about 2 miles. The space ship, resembling more a giant air liner than a rocket as we imagine it today, will run along this ramp, without switching on its motors, drawn by an appropriate vehicle. Once it reaches the end of the ramp it will take off like a stone being hurled from a sling. Then the turbo jets suspended from the wings will come into action. They will raise the giant bird into the air, constantly increasing the speed until an altitude of about 12 miles and a speed of 800 m.p.h. is reached. On reaching this speed motors will be detached from the large wings and descend to earth by drogue parachutes. In their place the ram jets in the wing will come into action. At an altitude of about 30 miles, during which the ship has reached a speed of 3,000 m.p.h. they will be detached together with the greater part of the wing which will no longer give lift, or as tanks for the propellant. The ship will at once lose its aeroplane form and will now look like a space rocket. Now the motor rockets will be started; these will increase its speed still further and drive it higher into space. Possibly two or three motors will be switched on in succession but the first will have already carried it high up where there is no atmosphere. As soon as the ship has developed escape velocity it will already be on its first stage to the stars.

Developing his idea, Varvarov thinks that the change from one type of motor to the other could be made in the future by changing ships instead of by jettisoning the motors. The space ship will be transformed into a series of aeroplanes designed to fly at various altitudes and at various speeds. After accomplishing their task they will descend to earth piloted by their own crews.

Varvarov's idea of changing the type of motor at various stages certainly has a rational foundation. Today we already possess plans of space rockets in an advanced state of construction using this particular idea of boosters. The International Press speaks of plans for a stepped rocket for launching another artificial satellite; during the first stage jet motors similar to those used in aircraft will be used. This will allow the oxygen to be taken from the air during the initial stages of the journey instead of being carried in the ship, thus considerably decreasing the weight of a stepped rocket at take off.

The Liquid Propellant Stepped Rocket

The basic motor of the space ship of the near future will run on liquid propellant. Ziolkowsky already suggested this in 1903. Forty years later a motor burning liquid propellant carried a rocket to a height of 150 miles. Today this height has been quadrupled.

The answer is simple: the designers have been unable to find any substantial modification even 50 years after his invention.

The rocket carries as much combustible as carburant in its body. Naturally they are contained in different tanks. As carburetant, alcohol is generally used—methyl or ethyl and more rarely petrol. For the combustile, oxygen is usual.[4]

Let us examine, for example, the construction of the V2. Two tanks—containing alcohol and oxygen fill the base of the rocket.

From these tanks, tubular pipes lead to the combustion chamber. These tubes contain powerful pumps which have to feed the combustion chamber with 325 lbs. of carburetant per second of the motor's life. They are set in motion by a small gas turbine motor running on peroxide of hydrogen.

The peroxide of hydrogen for the gas turbine is contained in a special capsule. From this, it passes into a small combustion chamber where under the action of sodium permanganate it is rapidly transformed into gas. This mixture, which has a relatively high temperature and pressure, works the turbines of the pumps. These carry the oxygen into the combustion chamber. The alcohol is first pumped across the opposite cavity which surrounds the nozzle and the combustion chamber acting as a coolant. If this were not done the walls of the combustion chamber and the nozzle would melt. In practice the temperature of the gas in the combustion

[4] See preceding note. Also, it is seldom that the amount of oxidizer carried equals the amount of fuel. Here are the weight ratios for the three cases the author proposes: oxygen/methyl alcohol, 1.15; Oxygen/ethyl alcohol, 1.50; and oxygen/petrol, 2.26. Depending on the oxidizer and fuel used, these ratios can go as high as 12.6 or as low as 0.076. (Ref., Bell Aircraft Corp.'s "Pocket Data for Rocket Engines.")

chamber reaches 3000° and that of the walls not more than 1000°.

Having ensured the cooling of the hottest part of the motor, the alcohol passes into the combustion chamber from diffusers in the rear part. Tiny sprays surround the main diffuser across which the oxygen passes.

At each second more than 350 lbs. of combustible material—alcohol and oxygen enter the combustion chamber. The incandescent gases rush towards the exhaust through a widened nozzle. The speed of the gas expulsion in the modern rocket motor exceeds 6,500 ft. per second. A motor of this type develops a thrust of many thousand lbs. After functioning for some seconds it raises the speed of the rocket to between 100 and 150 m.p.h.

In the pointed nose of the rocket's streamlined body is housed the payload. In the post war years this has consisted of instruments to survey the upper atmosphere. As we have seen, the rocket motor is almost as simple in construction as the ram jet. It too lacks mobile parts, if we exclude the pumps and the small turbine to set them in motion.

This in all probability will be the motor which will at first carry instruments and subsequently men on trips into space. But the distant future of interplanetary travel will probably lie in the atomic rocket.

The Atomic Rocket

Ziolkowsky's successor, J. Kondratink proposes to substitute for the oxygen used by the former ozone, an oxygen with triatomic molecules, a far more active combustible agent.[5] He also proposes to add solid to the liquid propellants, burning metals in the combustion chamber of the jet motor. But none of these carburetants really solve the problem. Today a combustible exists which could ensure the departure of a rocket from the earth its landing on another planet and return to earth without refueling or overburdening the space ship. This is the atomic combustible.

But this possesses a series of specific particularities which cast doubts as to its practical use.

At the moment of fission of the uranium atom, so-called gamma rays are radiated in all directions; they possess a great penetrating power and have a deleterious effect on the human organism. We have not as yet found any means of defense from these rays beyond the protection afforded by a thick concrete shield. The weight of a similar shield represents several tons per square yard of surface. To find an efficient means of safeguarding oneself against these rays is one of the as yet unsolved problems, and unless a solution be found we can rule out the atomic rocket.

On the splitting of the uranium atom its fragments are dispersed in all directions at a speed of many thousands of miles per second. The kinetic energy of these fragments is transformed into thermic energy and the metal of the reactor—this is the name of the structure

[5] J. Kondratink is given as Yu. V. Kondratyuk in 1956 *RAND review* of *Soviet astronautics*. RAND also confirms that Kondratink proposed use of ozone as a highly active oxidizer. (I believe author is misleading in calling it a "combustible agent.") Note that the oxidizer fluorine, for one, is even more active than ozone. Safety hazards have limited use of either of these molecular elements. (See United States Air Force *Project RAND Research Memorandum*, June 21, 1956, *A Casebook on Soviet Astronautics*, by F. J. Krieger.)

which the artificially induced reaction from the fission takes place—becomes overheated. The reactor must constantly be subjected to intensive cooling. The heat is absorbed by the coolant is all we have as yet managed to employ usefully. Neither the radiated energy given off at the moment of the splitting of the atom nor the kinetic energy of the fragments of the nuclei have as yet been controlled or transformed into any other kind of energy.

The plans of atomic motors already discussed by the Press are all based on the assumption that the thermic energy alone is utilizable. All these plans envisage carrying in the space ship, apart from the atomic combustible, a large amount of a substance which, heated to the highest temperature of the atomic reactor, can be eliminated through the exhaust. Similary they also envisage the sole possibility of using the thermic energy generated by the explosion. At the same time all these plans foresee the need for carrying in addition a large reserve of some intermediary heated substance at the expense of that energy which, after having been raised to a high temperature by the reactor, passes through the exhaust and is ejected in the same way as gas is ejected from a liquid propellant.

According to one of these plans the atomic space ship will have the passengers' cabin in its nose while the entire central part will be filled with the intermediary substance. To this end hydrogen could be used, a good thermic conductor and easily raised to a high temperature.

In the rear part of the rocket will be housed the atomic reactor. The tanks with the intermediary substance thus act as a protective shield against the gamma rays emitted by the reactor. The heat produced in the reactor is transmitted to the hydrogen whose incandescent jet, as in the case of an ordinary jet motor, escapes through the nozzle.

The thermic exchange between the reactor and the hydrogen is one of the most complicated and least experimented elements of this plan. In actual fact, the reactor must transmit to the hydrogen enormous quantities of heat in order to heat the jet in those few seconds in which contact is made up to 8-10,000°. In addition an intensive cooling must be assured to all parts of the motor which naturally could not stand such a temperature. To raise hydrogen to this temperature the reactor itself would have to have a higher temperature still. The idea of thermic exchange is a fascinating one. Uranium heated in the reactor until it has become gaseous, is injected slowly into the exchange chamber which is not unlike an ordinary combustion chamber. The gaseous uranium which has a quite high temperature, communicates its heat to the hydrogen and condenses in tiny drops of liquid metal which are oxydized by the flow of hydrogen and carried into the enlarged nozzle of the motor.

During its passage through the nozzle the speed of the jet constantly increases and it begins to cool. During the cooling process even more heat is imparted to the uranium which, during this movement from liquid becomes solid metal. The minute particles of this uranium having a slight lag continue to move towards the exhaust. But uranium is too costly to allow it to be lost in the role of a motive substance. A swirling movement acts on the hydrogen and uranium jets in the nozzle. Centrifugal force thrusts the weighty particles of the

Chapter Five

IN SPACE

A World Without Gravity

THE strata of the earth's surface are an open book to geologists. By observing the successive layers of clay, sand, or chalk on the high bank of a river or in a deep ravine he can tell the whole history of the locality, the various changes of climate it has endured and the rise and fall of the level of the earth which has emerged. From remains of bones and fossil shells he can reconstruct the aspect of the oldest inhabitants of the earth and the approximate date when they dwelt on it.

The rare remains of prehistoric algae, sea urchins, sponges and other simple forms of life, which the geologist finds in the earth, date from the protozoic period of the history of the earth's crust. These remains tell the story of a thousand million years.

The fossil remains of certain shells which are found in

enormous quantities—the ammonites—date from about 150 million years ago; the belemnites are younger, a mere 10 million years old.

A few hundred thousand years ago man appeared on the earth as nature evolved.

For millions of years life adapted itself to terrestrial conditions. Naturally these conditions have undergone variations; certain species adapted to certain conditions have become extinct and been replaced by others. But we can safely say that a whole series of factors determining this or that quality acquired by human organisms living on the earth have hardly modified over very lengthy periods of time. Thus, for example, the earth's power of attraction, the duration of day and night, the arrival of the seasons, the atmospheric pressure, the intensity of the magnetic field etc., have not varied.

The human organism has adapted itself to these conditions. The first space journey taken by man will be the first occasion upon which he finds himself outside the influence of the constant factors ruling on earth. How will his body stand up to these new conditions?

Until quite recent times the problem never came under consideration. Today, however, it is absolutely essential to find out whether man can stand the weightlessness of space before undertaking such a voyage.

Actually all the organs of our bodies are adapted to be in constant movement in a determined direction, under the influence of the force of gravity. We stand, walk or lie down. But if we lie head downwards the blood rushes to the brain.[1] In olden times certain torture existed: a man was crucified head downwards. This was deemed less cruel than normal crucifixion: the man soon

[1] Under zero gravity, would blood rush to the brain?

died from the rush of blood to the head. How can man stand the absence of this force of gravity? Some biologists maintain that a rush of blood to the head will result, giddiness and death; others insist that he will suffer no more than a slight feeling of sea sickness at the outset. Experiments must be made. We must study the behaviors of human organisms similar to our own in a condition of artificially created weightlessness.

In our laboratories we can create the most disparate conditions: in hothouses we can reproduce the damp heat of the tropics; subject various liquids in a cylinder to colossal pressure in order to study compression: from the plates of a giant condenser we can obtain a magnetic field of almost incredible intensity.[2] But no laboratory exists for the study of imponderability.[3] Weight is a manifestation of the force of terrestrial attraction. We cannot free ourselves from it, for it is omnipresent.

There exists one spot on this earth where bodies have no weight. Nevertheless it is out of reach of those who would study the question, being 4,000 miles below the surface at the center of the earth. Here the attraction of the whole earth mass acts equally in all directions, neutralizing itself on any body placed there.

Perhaps one day in the far future and long after he has visited all the planets of the solar system man will penetrate into the bowels of the earth and build an imponderability laboratory there. But by this time there will not be such an urgent need for one.

Scientists have, however, discovered a method of creating conditions of weightlessness even if only for a few seconds, without having to sink a shaft 4,000 miles. The

[2] Plates build up static charge, coils give the magnetic field.
[3] "Imponderability"—probably dictionary term for weightlessness.

following experiment was carried out. A few mice and a monkey were launched in a rocket, to a height of 30 miles. When the motors were cut, and the rocket began to fly by inertia before falling, its passengers were in a state of weightlessness. At the moment of free fall the body weighs nothing. People who go up in a lift can feel the partial loss of weight of their bodies. If the lift cabin, totally unsupported, began to descend in free fall, he would feel a total loss of weight. In fact weight is no more than the pressure of a body on a support, and in this case the support, the floor of the cabin, under the force of gravity escapes from under him at the same velocity as himself.

The mice used in the experiment were placed in a glass ball and the monkey was lashed to a rubber cushion. They were kept in focus by an automatic Press cine-camera. Each of their movements during the experiment was recorded. Automatic instruments measured the body temperature of the monkey, the heart beats etc. When the rocket began to make its descent a parachute opened and the first astronauts returned safely to earth.

The results of this experiment were very encouraging. The animals showed no trace of cardiac or nervous disturbances. But the flight had lasted only a few seconds. A gymnast can of course remain head downwards for some time. But what if a state of zero g lasts for a considerable time? Doctors can give no reply to this question. On the other hand space ship designers volunteer a reply.

"Let us admit," they say, "that the human body acts normally at zero g." But how difficult it would be to work in such conditions. The astronaut would have to be strapped to his seat for otherwise, at the least movement, he would fly up to the ceiling. The map on which he made his entries would have to be sewn or stuck to the table. All the objects in the cabin would have to be firmly secured. And many other peculiar things would happen in zero g. If you accidentally upset a little water it would fly through the air in the form of small balloons, would get into the man's respiratory channels and soak various objects. It would be difficult to kindle flame: the gas needed to produce combustion would not reach far enough and would die. Perhaps it would be difficult to breathe: the air exhaled would not be absorbed sufficiently by the rest of the air. It would be hard to boil water or to fry a steak.

No, continues the designer, it would be better to create an artificial gravity in the cabin. If we make the space ship revolve on its own axis, centrifugal force will replace gravity. Therefore we will not definitely cut out the motor but make the ship move continuously at acceleration which will also compensate for the loss of gravity.

A Variety of Rays

We often hear the expression, "as transparent as air." The air of course does possess a great degree of transparency. If it were not mixed with particles of dust and tiny drops of condensed water it would be difficult to deny that the air was not perfectly transparent. Sometimes remote objects are seen as though through a sky blue veil. We do not often stare into the distance and thus we do not always realize how far from transparent the air is.

Aviators speak very differently on this subject. They are often forced to observe objects on the horizon and this blue veil often impedes a clear view. They know how rare it is to find clear air without cloud, dust or mist.

The air covers the earth with a thick layer. We might say that we were living at the bottom of an ocean of air. The air, the atmosphere, allows a large percentage of the sun rays to reach the earth. But although transparent in the visible part of the spectrum the atmosphere is absolutely opaque at certain other parts of it.

The fiery ball of the Sun sheds out enormous quantities of energy uninterruptedly in all directions in space. This radiation—solar radiation—consists of rays of different wave lengths. Catch a sunbeam in the three-sided glass prism and it will be broken up into a multicolored strip—the spectrum. The colors range from red to blue; all of them therefore are contained in the white ray. These colors differ by the length of their waves. But the sun's rays are not limited to this visible in the solar spectrum. With the help of special instruments it can be proved that there are also infra red rays at one end of the scale. They can be revealed in a thermometer; the mercury will rise, owing to these infra red rays. Photographic film registers the presence of further invisible rays at the other end of the spectrum—the ultra violet rays.

In recent years it has been discovered that the Sun also sends out other rays of different wave lengths, including X rays.

The surface of the Sun, swept by hurricanes of incandescent gas hurls into space vast clouds of small corpuscles of a certain substance. On approaching the Earth these particles enter the magnetic field and are attracted towards the poles. There, penetrating the upper atmosphere they produce the fantastic spectacle known as the Aurora Borealis.

The earth receives a radiation of 70-20% (according to the height of the Sun above the horizon) of the whole of solar radiation. The remainder is retained by the atmosphere. The atmosphere, in particular, absorbs the ultra violet rays. At an altitude of 12-35 miles the air contains a large quantity of ozone. This layer of ozone absorbs and egulfs nearly all the ultra violet rays. Only a very small proportion of them reach the earth.

Some fifty years ago amateur wireless operators were struck by a curious phenomenon. When working with short waves, reception at short distances faded away to zero. In contrast, it became much greater over long distances. No one could explain the reason for these zones of silence. The secret lay in the non-transparence of air. The radio waves were reflected by the upper strata and fell back to earth; in the zone where they fell they once more became audible.

For many years scientists have been busy studying cosmic rays. These contain more energy than all the other known rays and a colossal penetrating capacity. The sun is not the sole fount of these rays; they assail the earth from all directions with a mean intensity varying according to the hour of the day or the season. When scientists began to investigate the nature of these rays, they came to the conclusion that they were not really rays penetrating the lower strata of the atmosphere but a rain of fragments of nuclear atom,[4] smashed to particles

[4] Not "fragments of nuclear atom," but rather protons and atomic nucleii stripped of their electrons. (Ref., *Satellite!* E. Bergaust and W. Beller, Hanover House, 1956, p. 90.)

in their precipitous flight through the upper atmosphere. In this case the atmosphere protects us from the penetration of these powerful and mysterious messengers from space.

What will happen when the space ship flies beyond the limits of the atmosphere and is exposed to all the fury of solar radiation and perhaps to other radiations of which we are as yet ignorant—radiations which arrive entirely retained by our atmosphere? What effect will they have on the human body? Could the torrents of cosmic rays cause the complete destruction of the space ship?

The scientists have carried out an experiment: they have sent mice and rabbits up to great heights in the cabin of a stratosphere balloon, leaving them there for a certain length of time. Rockets, too, have carried animals to a height of more than 60 miles for a few seconds.[5] But science is still not in the position to give a reply to the question of the influence of solar radiation on living organisms and in particular on the human body.

We know that ultra violet rays which hardly reach the earth's surface have a great physiological effect on living organisms. Their effect can be seen on the golden brown skin of a sunburned human being. Being exposed to small quantities of these rays greatly increases the growth of lambs[6] and calves as any cattle farmer knows, but in large quantities they are fatal. Were the protective covering of ozone to disappear, the earth's surface would become an arid lifeless desert.

[5] The U.S. has conducted many high-altitude experiments with animals.

[6] These rays increase the growth of vitamin D, which in turn affects the growth of animals.

It will not be unduly difficult to safeguard the passenger of a space ship from the deadly effects of ultraviolet rays because many substances are refractory to them. Ordinary glass in particular is almost impenetrable for them. Ultra violet lamps are therefore made of quartz instead of glass.

It will be far more complicated to find a defense against cosmic rays. Their influence on living organisms and materials has not so far been sufficiently studied. They will be in the near future.

The Heat of the Sun

What will be the general effects of the entire flood of solar radiation? Will the space ship be burnt up by the rays of the sun and destroyed as Icarus was when he approached too near it? Or will the contrary occur? Will the cold of outer space penetrate the walls of the ship and kill everyone inside?

We can answer this question. The passengers of a space ship, within certain limits, will be able to maintain a desired temperature inside the cabin. The sun will take care of this. Does it not heat the earth which is really no more than a gigantic space ship?

Take a slab of brightly polished metal, covered with a thin layer of chromium or nickel and place it next to an identical slab covered with opaque black paint. After 5 minutes touch the two slabs: the polished one will be as cold as it was before, but the black-painted one will be hot from the sun's rays. The polished slab has reflected the best part of the rays and has not therefore become heated. The black slab on the other hand has absorbed the greater part of the rays and grown hot.

If we could construct a completely black ball, so that it would absorb all the rays of the sun which fell on it, and place it in space near the Sun making it rotate at speed on its own axis, its tempreature would be 3°. An absolutely black cylinder of a length corresponding to five radiuses with its surface turned towards the sun would on the earth's orbit have a temperature exceeding 12°.[7]

By approaching them to the Sun, the temperature of these bodies would increase rapidly. On the orbit of Venus the ball would rise in heat to 52° and the cylinder to 64°; their temperatures would be 171° and 187° respectively. On the other hand, on the orbit of Mars the temperatures would be 49° and 41°. But this is intense cold! How could a man live and work in such temperatures in space?

. . . Now the vast ship leaves the earth and moves majestically towards far distant Pluto in the domain of eternal ice, darkness and cold.

This outermost planet is 40 times further from the Sun than the Earth and receives 1,600 times less calories per unit on its surface. Already on Uranus, which is twice as near the sun as Pluto, the temperature of the illuminated part descends to −183°. On the surface of Pluto we could expect a temperature of less than −210°. There, the astronauts will see rocks and mountains of solidified carbon dioxide, rivers of nitrogen and liquid oxygen flowing in deep beds hollowed out in the rocks, blue clouds of oxygen and nitrogen in an atmosphere of hydrogen and helium.

In all probability Pluto does not possess great quan-

[7] Are these temperatures centigrade, fahrenheit, kelvin or rankine? Whatever they are, they seem inconsistent with facts. The author nowhere in book gives units to temperatures.

tities of those, which liquefy at low temperatures, to form an atmosphere. It is probably a cold, dead planet, its surface covered with a thick layer of ice formed of oxygen and nitrogen. The sun reflects on the transparent rocks of ice like a great star, powerless at this great distance to melt the eternal ice.

The space ship speeds towards the bounds of our solar system at a speed many times exceeding escape velocity. It covers more than 60 miles per second in space. But even at this speed it would take 2 years to reach Pluto.

Everything has been taken into account to make the surroundings of the astronauts agreeable. The body of the ship is painted an opaque black, designed to absorb the greater part of the sun's rays. The cabin is insulated but the insulation can be removed from the side turned to the sun and reinforced on the side which remains in the shade. The inside of the ship can also be heated by fuel brought from the earth. The powerful insulation will allow a maximum economy of fuel. Every lb. of combustible is too precious in outer space at a distance of millions of miles from the earth. It will serve for landing or in a case when avoiding action has to be taken from some stray asteroid whose attraction makes the ship deviate from its course. Economy is vital.

The captain of the ship is the undisputed master of the limitless spaces. On one side—the shady side away from the sun—the surfaces are covered with a thick layer of black like the rest of the ship. The other side, of shining metal, gleams. The outside of this huge caravel is warmed by the sun while the other is at the mercy of the cosmic cold. The difference in temperature exceeds 300-150° according to the distance from the sun. This difference in temperature is exploited by the use of electric energy from thermal elements.

It has been found that if you take two wires of different metal and solder the ends, heating one of the soldered points and cooling the other, thus creating a difference of temperature, an electric current will pass through the wires. This phenomenon has been applied for some time to take accurate measurements of temperature.

On this principle, the crew of the space ship will create a helio-electric station in the ship and use the energy into which the sun's rays have been transformed for heating and lighting the ship. Astronauts will have nothing to fear from the cosmic cold!

A Hothouse in Space

In order to remain alive the human organism has to absorb in 24 hours under physical working conditions 140 grams of albumen, a similar quantity of fat, about 400 grams of carbohydrates and the same amount if mineral salts and vitamins.[8] In addition to this man requires 2-5 liters of water a day. From these figures it will be seen that a man's daily ration attains a weight of 7-10 lbs. To this must be added the amount of oxygen he breathes which will amount to another 2½ lbs.

Ten lbs. in 24 hours per person represents a supply of 300 lbs. per month, and several tons if the space journey is to last a year. Ten years must not be ruled out once man decides to visit the planets beyond the Moon, Venus and Mars. In this event the supplies would amount to hundreds of tons.

In actual fact this is not the true position. Only for

[8] "Albumen" should be "protein." His figures are overly conservative.

short trips, such as to the Moon and back, will provisions, water and oxygen be carried. For longer forays it will be rational to organize complete sources of supply necessary to daily life in the ship itself.

Water constitutes the least of the problems. It must be accepted that the human body expels more water than it consumes.[9] The excess of water expelled over intake is about 400 grams in 24 hours. All that is required to purify this water will be a distillation plant. The energy for the evaporation will be furnished by the helioelectric plant we have already mentioned.

The problem of the extraction of water from the air is more serious. Man as he breathes exhales an air enriched by considerable moisture as we can see if we breathe on a cold mirror; a blemish of condensed steam will appear. In winter the moisture of human breath can be seen on the window panes. To remove and recover the superfluous moisture in the air, it will be systematically passed through a refrigerator where the water will condense. If we could obtain a temperature of $-78°$ or less in this refrigerator, we could also purify it of carbon dioxide which liquefies at such a temperature.

A new expenditure of energy! And this time to function a refrigerator! No, the refrigerator will have no need of energy. The cosmic cold will be at the disposal of the passengers of a space ship. They need only place the refrigerator lead outside the ship on the shady side, for a temperature of $-100°$, $-150°$, $-200°$ to be reached with ease.

[9] The fact that the human body expels more water than it consumes is merely part of the metabolic process in which water vapor is a by-product.

Thus the problems of water supply and air purification have been solved. More complicated is how to establish the circulation of oxygen and foodstuffs.

The earth's atmosphere, according to scientists, once contained a large quantity of carbon dioxide. The plants were instrumental in purifying it. It is the main matter upon which they feed, owing to the constitution of their texture, stems and leaves. In absorbing the carbon dioxide plants use only one of its components, the carbon, returning the oxygen to the air. The vast beds of fossilized carbon which are to be found in every continent are merely the carbon which has been extracted from the air by plant life.

The vitality of animal organisms, on the other hand, is usually based on absorption of the oxygen and the expulsion of carbon dioxide. The latter gas is formed in every process of combustion, either in a steam engine, in the cylinder of internal combustion or the chambers of jet engines. But on sunny days, when the sun's rays make the bright foliage of the plants gleam, the reverse process takes place; the oxygen is eliminated and the carbon dioxide absorbed. These two processes balance each other and the quantity of carbon dioxide in the earth's atmosphere remains constant.

This process can be imitated. Take earth and the seeds of a certain plant, peas, for example, and place them in a glass vase. Moisten the earth sufficiently, seal the vase hermetically and turn it upside down. The little world, isolated in the glass, is then placed on the windowsill.

The seeds of the plants in the vase will germinate and develop normally until the green of the foliage fills the entire vessel. There is no doubt that the plants will con-

sume the carbon dioxide as they do on Earth. The latter
is recreated by the vitality of the worms which live in
the soil and feed on fallen leaves, dead roots, branches
etc. In the vase we have created a complete circulatory
system of foodstuffs, water and oxygen.

Why could the same system not be employed in a
space ship? It would only be necessary to carry the in-
stallations necessary to grow plants. The greenhouse
could be of very modest proportions; a few square feet
of foliage, taking into account the intense increase of
solar radiation in space, would suffice to reconstitute the
acidified exhalations of a man.

It has been suggested that seaweed might be used to
reconstitute oxygen. In this event, instead of a greenhouse, the space ship could carry a kind of aquarium
with transparent and opaque sides close together where,
in the narrow interstices the seaweed could grow on the
transparent sides. These aquaria would be turned to the
sun. Air would be systematically pumped through the
water and in its passage would lose its carbon dioxide,
and at the same time enrich itself with oxygen.

Today it is difficult to forecast how our terrestrial
plants would adapt themselves to conditions in space,
how they would develop in a state of weightlessness,
subjected to intensive solar radiations etc. But in all
probability it would be just as possible to select plants
capable of bearing fruit in the new surroundings as it
is on earth. Taking into account the increased solar
radiation and its permanency it would be reasonable to
suppose that the maximum production on earth per
square ft. of greenhouse could be surpassed. Moreover
to ensure the change of oxygen as well as the food sup-

ply for the astronauts would need only a few hundred
or thousand square feet.

Let us take a look at the space greenhouse. It is joined
to the cabin of the ship by a long corridor, the walls of
which run in a direction which will give the ship and
the greenhouse a common center of gravity so that the
surface of the latter will always remain perpendicular
to the rays of the sun.

From afar the greenhouse looks like an immense frying
pan covered with a transparent lid of plastic material.[10]
Its transparent side is turned towards the sun while on
the opaque part are various layers of netting, also made
of plastic, among which is a certain amount of soil for
the roots of the plants.

But these will draw their nourishment not so much
from this soil as from the water which flows continuously
from one side of this field. As well as water the plants
will receive all the pulverized refuse. By the effect of
centrifugal force the water flows slowly through the
earth keeping the roots of the plants moist.

Air vents and fans will assure a continuous flow of
air through the greenhouse. The air, passing through a
carbon filter, enriched by oxygen and ozone, formed by
the effects of the ultra violet rays not retained by the
plastic glass of the greenhouse, will then pass into the
ship's living quarters. From here the consumed air returns into the greenhouse, rich in carbon dioxide and
poor in oxygen.

[10] A grandiose scheme that the nutritionist Dr. Harold Wooster,
Air Force Office of Scientific Research, Washington, D. C., feels
could be done simply by a small amount of algae subjected to in-
termittent fluorescent light rays.

The plants clinging by their roots to the netting extend their stems and branches into the air towards the common axis of the ship and the greenhouse. Their leaves are turned towards the sun.

Equipped with such a greenhouse, the ship could remain in space for an indeterminate period without renewing its supplies as the earth has to do on its eternal path round the sun.

But perhaps it will be unnecessary to trail in space the colossal structure which this greenhouse represents. Its enormous surface would prove an excellent target for meteorites which could easily destroy it.

Some scientists consider it possible to ensure the circulation of supplies in the space ship by means of cheminal reaction, by producing synthetic foods from refuse etc.

It is difficult to refute them. Such great successes have been achieved by modern science in the field of producing synthetic products from all manner of organic substances, some of which can be used for human consumption. The prodigious advance of chemistry will perhaps allow us in the near future to produce albumen and fats synthetically in limited quantities so that all essential foodstuffs could be supplied to the space ship without the aid of a greenhouse. But this would only be possible if the laboratory where the synthetic products were made could be supplied with sufficient energy.

In fact, in consuming food products, in transforming the complex molecules of albumens, fats and carbohydrates into simpler forms we use up the energy produced: we "burn," so to speak, food products in our organism. In this respect the body resembles a steam boiler in which the energy freed by combustion is used for heating water and steam. The gases emitted by the chimney and the ashes which fall into the grate contain all the substances which were burnt. They merely lack the energy which was contained in the molecules of the fuel. To recreate these complex molecules from their simplified state—gas and ashes—is possible by restoring the lost energy. In precisely the same manner great energy will be needed from the inverse syntheses of foodstuffs.

But where can we obtain this energy? From the Sun, by building a grandiose helio-electric station. But it would be quite a task to build a station of this size; it would have to be much larger than our greenhouse. All the known engineering methods for exploiting the energy from solar rays in synthetics are far less economical than plant action. Could the foodstuffs produced compete with those vegetables?

We do not yet know which point of view will prevail. It is probable that at the outset the greenhouses will give better results. Later with advances in chemistry and helio-energy, artificial methods will start to compete with the natural, the utility co-efficient of the synthetic laboratory will approach that of the tiny, and in certain respects still mysterious laboratories—the green cells of plants. It is doubtful whether they could be surpassed. But the specialists among space gardeners will not remain idle. They will endeavor to produce plants endowed with a high utility coefficiency.

But this is a field of pure conjecture and supposition. It is our task to indicate the possible ways of solving

various problems, selecting those which today appear
capable of solution.

Space Projectiles

On clear nights one often sees meteors streaking across
the velvet sky. In some years they arrive in their hosts
like a shower of rain. Without reaching the Earth the
fragments evaporate without a trace.

We cannot see these meteors during the day but they
continue to fall on the illuminated part of the earth.
This has been proved by radar. The waves cannot be
picked for most of the meteorites are far too small, but
their track appears on the cathode ray tube.

The dimensions of meteorite bodies vary considerably.
In the most part they are mere grains of substance
weighing 1 gram or less, but they can be larger. In certain cases they do not have time to vaporize and fall
on the earth in the form of "bolts out of the blue." A
meteorite weighing 60 tons recently fell in South West
Africa and an even larger one fell in Siberia in 1947.
The total weight of its fragments—it broke up in the
air—has been calculated at about 100 tons. Naturally the
larger part of the mass vaporized into the form of
dust and was dispersed in the earth's atmosphere. In
space its dimensions were considerably larger.

The sum total of meteorites is legion. Every hour
more than 20,000 of them break up in the atmosphere
which acts as a powerful shield to protect the earth
from these unwelcome space visitors. Were there no atmosphere, the earth's surface would be subjected to a
terrible bombardment which would possibly reduce it to

dust in the same way that the moon's surface has been destroyed. The average speed of meteorites in space is exceedingly high. At the moment of entering the atmosphere they are computed to be travelling at between 10-40 miles per second.

Meteorites possibly constitute the greatest danger to astronauts.[11] A projectile fired by a rifle has a velocity of about 2,900 ft. per second. It it hits an obstacle of steel it shatters and becomes too hot to touch. Shells have a greater velocity and on hitting an obstacle melt and scatter in a liquid state. Increasing the speed, sudden braking can cause immediate vaporization of its entire matter and an explosion as though it had been made of nitroglycerine instead of steel or lead. Calculations shows that a similar explosion will occur on the instantaneous arrest of a projectile travelling at about 2½ miles per second.

Meterorites have a speed ten times greater than this. Should one of them hit the metal casing of a space ship it would be halted immediately. The entire kinetic energy of its motion would be transformed into thermic energy causing it to vaporize without a trace. It would also vaporize that part of the space ship's casing which was subjected to the blow and destroy anything that crossed its path. A meteorite body weighing 1 gram travelling at a speed of 20 miles per second could rip off the steel casing of a space ship to a weight of 12-25 lbs.

Meteorites are met with at a certain frequency in space. According to Professor Staniukovich's calculations,

[11] "Meteorites" are found on earth; "meteors" are found in space. Regardless, most authorities do not agree that meteors are the greatest danger to aeronauts. Cosmic rays, for one, may be far more lethal.

meteors weighing less than a gram travel at 60-300 miles apart. When one considers that a journey to Mars lasts some months it is obvious that an encounter with one of them cannot be overlooked.

It is too early today to discuss the defense measures against meteorites: the problem has been insufficiently studied. The larger ones could easily be avoided by means of radar which would signal their position to the space ship. But larger meteorites are comparatively rare. We have mentioned the consequences of an encounter with a tiny meteorite and, since no radar has yet been devised sensitive enough to pick them up, we shall perhaps have recourse to a double casing for the ship: a flexible layer, then a vacuum and a second layer which will be the actual side of the ship.

Interplanetary Routes

Before take off an aircraft pilot studies the stretch to be covered on his maps. The problem of navigation in space is far more difficult.

The pilot of an aircraft does not have to worry about learning the earth. By day, when there is no cloud, he can see the ground distinctly from his cockpit; at night or in fog he has his altimeter and radar beam. Nor will his engine permit him to fly higher than his ceiling.

In short he has only two possibilities of going off his course—to port or starboard. The pilot of a space ship, however, has infinite possibilities: all ways are open to him; port, starboard, up or down and all their combinations.

The length of a voyage in a modern aircraft will not

exceed a few thousand miles and will never exceed 25,000 miles—the circumference of the globe.

The shortest journey of a space ship, to the nearest body in space, the Moon, 250,000 miles away, will take a whole week.[12]

On earth the airfields are perforce stationary. The point to which the pilot steers has a fixed geographical position on the surface of the earth and does not move, even if the pilot decides to postpone his journey for a few hours or even until the following day.

In space, the destinations—the planets—do not have fixed positions. They move along gigantic ellipses round the Sun, and share its orbit round the galaxy. If an astronaut were to steer his vessel to a prefixed point with 24 hours delay earth time, he would no longer find his cosmodrome. If it happened to be Venus, the planet would have moved 400,000 miles away; in the case of Mars it would be 300,000 miles. As will be observed these displacements are on a cosmic scale!

Nevertheless, trips through space have already been worked out by scientists with great boldness of conception. Important work in this field has been carried out by A. Sternfeld, an enthusiastic astronaut who has popularized space travel.

The pilot of the space ship of the future has unrolled the huge chart of that part of the solar system he will cover on his journey: the plan covers an area of many square feet. Innumerable lines intersect on this white chart. It is difficult to find your way in this labyrinth.[13]

[12] Five days is the maximum time a direct voyage to the moon would take. (Ref., "Interplanetary Flight," Arthur C. Clarke, Harper & Brothers, p. 56.)

[13] Space craft will probably be navigated by automatic computers rather than by pilot judgment.

The two orbits of the planets in question—the Earth and Venus appear on it in the form of concentric ellipses. These are isobars sui generis—lines representing the measurements of the powerful attraction of the sun to which the ship will be subjected, as soon as it has escaped from the earth's thrall. Multi-colored lines represent the influence at a given point in space of the attraction of the various planets according to their positions on their own orbits. Through this apparent chaos, the pilot will trace the neat line of his flight.

He opens the large books of astronomical tables and sits down to make his calculations. As a start he has to choose the time of launching. This is not as simple as it appears. On earth one can set out on a journey at any hour and at any season. A man who fires at a stationary target does not have to think when to press the trigger. But one who fires at a moving target has to choose the exact moment to fire or else he will miss the target.

Choosing the moment for launching a space ship entails forecasting the respective positions of the planets so that the planet of destination will be found exactly at the given point of its orbit when the ship arrives.

This conjunctural position of the planets is not always to hand. It may be necessary to postpone the trip for two or three or perhaps even six months. For long periods the respective positions of the planets will be such that no communication between them will be possible. In the timetables of interplanetary flight there will be whole months when no space ship leaves the Earth and none will land. These will be the dead seasons. Only the use of the atomic motor could shorten them to any extent.

So the day of departure has been decided upon. Now

the hour has to be chosen. Nor is this as simple as it would appear. The pilot knows that his first task is to calculate the journey with the greatest economy of fuel. He knows that to reach the necessary speed, the ship has to exploit both the orbital and the axial rotation speeds of the earth.

Calculations show that from the point of view of consumption of energy, the most rational trajectory for interplanetary flight is the elliptical orbit described by the planets. To launch the ship along the arc of this ellipse, the pilot must give it a velocity of 7.8 miles per second. A part of this speed he can obtain from the earth's axial rotation. To do this he must take off at exactly mid-day when the sun is at its zenith. He must neither be late nor leave ahead of time. A. Sternfeld compares the launching of a space ship not only to a shot fired at a moving target but as a shot from a pitching ship. The gun aimer is at his periscope; the target sways in his binoculars. If he misses the precise moment to fire, the shell will fall short in the water or will fly beyond the target after describing a wide arc in the sky.

The launching direction is opposite to the movement of the earth. The pilot takes his pencil and draws a small circle on his plan—the Earth. It moves along its orbit at nearly 4 miles per second. The ship which has rashly left the earth, is soon suspended in space and moving ever further away. Its speed round the sun is 7 miles per second less than that of the earth. Finding itself subject to the mighty attraction of the sun it begins to fall slowly towards it.

But for a time the ship is also moving forwards, following the receding earth at a speed in excess of 10 miles per second. Thus it does not fall directly towards the sun but describes a gigantic arc in the field of its attraction. It is precisely this arc which should unite the two planets in question—the Earth and Venus.

Inch by inch the pilot traces this arc on his plan. The pencil comes to a halt. From this point onwards the ship will begin to feel the disturbing influence of Mars and Jupiter. The orbits of both these planets are pleasantly close to each other. The pilot makes a few calculations. Yes, the trajectory should be correct according to the rate of his motors. He records on his log the exact times when the motors will have to be switched on.

But now the red line—the arc of the ellipse—has approached the graph of Venus's orbit and has intersected it. Now comes the most important part of the journey —the landing.

Moving slowly along its trajectory under the attraction of the sun, the space ship is subject to the laws which Kepler the great arbiter of the skies discovered and which man has learnt to use for his own ends. In common with all the planets the ship's movement will be irregular. Nearing the sun its speed will undergo an acceleration. And when it approaches the orbit of Venus despite the fact that its speed will exceed that of the earth by more than 3 miles per second (while at the outset the speed remained considerably lower than that of the earth), its speed will be more than 2 miles per second faster than that of the planet of its destination.

The pilot studies the grandiose scene. The sun, gigantic in a black sky. A far off insignificant star, the Earth. Ahead the disc of the new planet increasing rapidly in size, mysterious Venus, the planet which so far no one has seen except through a telescope. It is always covered by a thick impenetrable veil of cloud.

At each second the ship's distance from this planet is reduced by 3 miles.

The pilot's pencil traces the last few inches of the flight. Now the attraction of Venus is beginning to be felt. The ship falls towards it like a stone hurled from a giant's sling, as though attracted by its goal. But it is still too soon to switch on the motors. Both on launching and landing the more rapid and intensive the braking, the greater will be the saving of fuel. This limit is represented only by the capability of the human body to withstand the overweight caused by the acceleration.

Perhaps braking can be avoided by the use of the motors. After making the necessary calculations, the pilot plans an alternative landing by braking in the atmosphere of Venus. There are all too many unknown factors; the composition, density and the depth of this atmosphere. But he must try to economize fuel . . . He bends over his tables once more.

Now the ship, like a huge tin fish, following the tangent of the atmosphere's surface, cleaves the dense opaque clouds. He must not enter too deeply into them because the braking would be too abrupt and the crew could not stand the pressure. Meteorites, those celestial stones which cleave the earth's rarified atmosphere at a height of 25-30 miles, often lose $2\frac{1}{2}$ miles per second in speed. The captain could lose 50 times this with his ship.

Hardly has he entered the atmosphere than he pulls out again. This is necessary for another reason. The casing of the ship can become excessively hot meeting with the atmosphere. The pilot recalls how meteorites vaporize as soon as they hit the atmosphere and flash across the sky like scarlet rockets at 1 mile per second. He has no intention of allowing his ship to become a shooting star above Venus. Therefore it is essential to pull his ship out of the atmosphere again and slow down to give it time to cool.

The space ship describes an arc of an elongated ellipse. But now its direction changes once more and, still following the tangent, it slips onto the atmosphere. The pilot calculates that now he will not have to expend fuel for his turn and will skillfully use the planet's attraction. Once more the ship emerges from the atmosphere into space. Exactly like a flying fish which for a moment dives into its natural element before a leap and a second plunge.

The flying fish has to keep submerging in order to get the speed for its leap. In the space ship, on the contrary, everything is being done to reduce speed.

At last this has been achieved: the speed is now insufficient for a further leap out of the atmosphere. The ship will complete its journey by planing slowly down through the dense atmosphere of Venus which vibrates with solar radiation, down towards the surface of the planet in search of a suitable place to land.

Pulling the ship's nose up abruptly, the pilot sets it down on Venus, the unexplored planet.

The protective window shields have been removed. The crew presses to the windows. The layer of cloud hides the view. Through a vent in the cloud changing color at every moment, and giving the whole landscape a fantastic and eerie character, swirl the cold flames of the Aurora Borealis. . . .

The pilot lays aside his red pencil and rolls up his chart. Now the automatic controls, which have followed his progress since leaving earth like a faithful watchdog, go into action . . .

According to the secientists this is more or less what one of the first interplanetary flights will be like. Space ships will of course gradually be perfected. Atomic energy will replace liquid propellant. How wonderful they will appear in comparison with the first slow, wretched space ships.

With the installation of jet atomic motors interplanetary flight will completely change. The pilot will no longer have to conserve energy and begrudge every drop of fuel. The speed will be increased by several times just as the aeroplane increased its speed on the change over from pistons to jets. The duration of the journeys will shrink from months to weeks. Now the elliptical trajectories will become parabolic and eventually the ship will fly in a direct line from planet to planet.

Chapter Six

THE STAGES OF THE GREAT OFFENSIVE

The Exploration of the Ionosphere

THE combined rocket V2, serving as booster and the WAC Corporal as the second step rose to a height of 250 miles above the earth. On another occasion the second step of the rocket rose to 435 miles.[1] Is this much or little?

At first sight it seems very little. A voyage to the Moon would mean a journey 600 times as long. Making a leap into the air, a man is nearer to the top of the highest mountain than this rocket was in respect to the moon. The journeys to Mars and Venus do not even allow a comparison.

[1] I can find no mention of a 435-mile flight with a V2 and a WAC Corporal in the literature. Reference is probably to the first flight of the WAC Corporal, which in October, 1945 reached 43.5 miles altitude.

We have already mentioned that the first stage is the most difficult. Furthermore, this step of 250 miles is more than 1/1000th of man's road to the Moon.

From the point of view of energy, a rocket capable of rising to 250 miles is already 1/9th of a space rocket. It develops 1/9th of the energy required to transform it into an artificial earth satellite.

From the point of view of speed, this rocket is 1/3rd of a space rocket; it has in actual fact a speed of slightly less than 1.56 miles per second. A body to become an earth satellite at an altitude of 300 miles has to be given a speed of 4,830 miles per second.[2]

As we can see, the leap of 250-275 miles was by no means insignificant.

Scientific innovations are never left to chance. What load was the first locomotive able to carry? 3.2 tons: 1/20th of the weight of one modern truck. What was the speed of Stephenson's first steam locomotive? When it reached a speed of 13 m.p.h. on its trials, the crowd threw their caps in the air and shouted "She flies like a bird!" Today an electrically driven train can travel on rails nearly 200 m.p.h. But who would dare to maintain that without Stephenson's work the modern railway engine would have appeared? These machines are an inevitable stage in scientific development which today has been far surpassed.

"We live on the threshold of space flight," said A. Sternfeld, the Soviet scientist to whom the astronaut owes so many bold ideas.

We must consider the first rocket that made a leap of 250 miles as the first explorer on the highway to the stars upon which man has now definitely set his foot.

[2] Not 4830 miles a second but 4.8 miles a second.

Particularly since these flights are not purely sporting events but sponsored by scientists with a view to increasing our knowledge of the upper atmosphere and outer space.

Fifteen years ago, the liquid propellant rocket, which today has reached the limits of the atmosphere, could not have risen more than a few miles above the earth. It was born in 1930 when Frederik Sander built and experimented with the first motors on jet principles with liquid propellant.[3] The exploration of the atmosphere had already become a fact through manned and sounding balloons.

The highest altitude reached by a manned balloon is 73,000 ft., when the Russian Osoaviahim I recorded this height in 1934. A year later the American explorer beat the Russian record by 154 ft.[4]

Sounding balloons have reached a far greater height.

Our knowledge of the upper atmosphere was obtained solely by observations of the Aurora Borealis, the explosion of meteors, the movements of cirrus cloud and the reflection of sound and radio waves.

Rockets enabled the frail apparatuses of science to be carried to a far greater height, furnishing us new ideas on the limits of the ionosphere. Today we know the temperature of the various strata of the atmosphere, the distribution of pressure, the speed and direction of the

[3] On March 16, 1926, Robert Goddard fired the first liquid-fueled rocket. It traveled 184 feet in 2.5 seconds.

[4] On this Russian balloon trip, all three crew members perished, so altitude reached is in doubt. Best guess of authorities is 72,000 feet. First balloon flight using sealed-cabin system was made in Germany by A. Piccard and P. Kipfer. On June, 1957, the American J. Kittinger ascended to 96,000 feet, and on August, 1957, U.S. Air Force Major D. Simons reached 102,000 feet.

winds at various distances from the Earth, the degree of ionization and the chemical composition of the gases.

Some of the information furnished by rockets came as a surprise and radically changed our hypotheses based on theoretical data, while others confirmed existing theories.

Thus the hypothesis that the composition of the upper atmosphere remains almost identical to that found at the earth's surface, has been confirmed.[5] According to some theoretical calculations on the contrary it was thought that its structure was a stratification with a prevalence of light gases at great altitudes such as hydrogen and helium, in the same way that nitrogen and oxygen prevail at surface level.

It was a surprise to find that the temperature of the upper air at 120 miles rose to 700°. Naturally, even at such a temperature, the air can neither burn nor heat an object which happens to be at that height. The atmosphere is too rarefied and the concept of temperature has acquired a significance to which we were unaccustomed. This axiom defines the mean speed of the motion of molecules. Another surprise was the existence at great altitudes of strong air currents, constant in direction.

The liquid propellant rocket was born during the Second World War.[6] The front lines encompassed Europe and Asia. In the offices of top secret designers, the brilliant idea of the Soviet scientist Ziolkowsky was hastily adapted to homicidal ends by Hitler's engineers.

[5] Composition of upper atmosphere differs from that of lower atmosphere—one instance: presence of free radicals in upper atmosphere. Air Force has a continuing study dealing with this phenomenon.

[6] See Chapter 3, Note 5.

In a remote spot on the Baltic, surrounded by a barrier of barbed wire, the supreme creation of man's in-
genuity, his ideas and the deductions of several generations of intelligent brains, crystallized into a gleaming
streamlined body carrying a motor with a thrust of half
a million h.p., capable of hurling it a distance of some
hundred miles.

It was a miracle of science and its greatest achievement. But it was suddenly disgraced by a crime. Instead
of intelligent, automatic instruments, a greenish yellow
mass of dormant death was placed in the nose of the
rocket. Its first flight was not for scientific purposes, to
advance the human race on the path of progress, but to
cause a murderous explosion in a populated part of
London.

Not until the end of the war did this rocket become a
scientific weapon. Now it carried beyond the clouds into
the ionosphere not compressed yellow death but instruments to explore and investigate cosmic rays.

Explosions were caused by means of the rocket, but
they were explosions in those upper regions where the
tracks of meteors can be observed. The scientists desired
to reproduce this natural phenomenon artificially, to
make models of meteors and create a rain of shooting
stars. This experiment was a failure and the artificial
rain never matured. Evidently the speed which could be
given to the fragments of the shells exploded was insufficient compared with that of a meteor. Or perhaps
there was some other reason. The fall of meteors and
their luminous trails is a phenomenon which has not
been sufficiently studied. It is possible, as V. Solianik believes, that in the formation of this trail the powerful
electric charge of the cosmic body plays a preponderant

part as it enters the atmosphere. This electric charge in the rarefied air produces ionization and the luminosity to the gases in a neon light. Or again the luminous trail of the meteor may be due to a combination of these causes.

Another experiment was brilliantly successful—the determination of the direction of the air currents. A device was fitted into the rocket which at fixed intervals would emit small clouds of powder. This was fine enough to remain suspended without dispersal despite the rarification of the air: a feather falling through this light air would not be passed by a lead balloon. These clouds of powder, lit up by the sun and therefore visible on earth through binoculars, were carried along by air currents of which few people knew the existence. Scientists turned their attention in particular to the electrical structure of the ionosphere: the concentration of the gas ions, the distribution of the strata of ionization etc. It is obvious that on these strata will depend the quality of future radio communication. Would it not be of the greatest interest to "contact" this "breath" by which radio waves are reflected?[7]

Many other experiments and studies of major importance to specialists have been and will continue to be carried out by launching rockets into the uppermost atmosphere.

The uppermost atmosphere! But traces of atmosphere have been observed at a height of 600 miles.

Correct. The exploration of these regions will be the next task for the high performance rocket. The liquid propellant rocket will enable man to discover the secrets

[7] U. S. Air Force has been bouncing radio waves off "artificial meteor trails" for years.

of the atmosphere, not only near the earth but at all strata and everywhere in space.

In the near future man will be making his researches on the confines of the atmosphere. There are, however, a whole series of researches which cannot be entrusted to instruments. Man himself will have to carry out these and to this end he will man the first rocket.

Ten Thousand Times Faster

Russia is boundless! On her northern islands and in the polar regions men wrap themselves in furs beneath the fairy spectacle of the Aurora Borealis. At the same moment a sub-tropical sun heats the southern regions where the cherry is in bloom and the children in bathing costumes pursue bright flower-like butterflies in the kolkhoz gardens.

The steel railway lines, the tarred roads and the invisible air lines connect the regions and cities of Russia. We can use any of these methods of transport to reach any particular city.

But not many years ago such communications did not exist. Barely half a century has passed since the flight of the first aeroplane[8] and not much longer since the first automobile. Prior to this, travel was on horseback or on foot.

How long does it take by various means of transport to travel from Vladivostock to Moscow?

[8] "Barely half a century has passed since the flight of the first aeroplane . . . Does this statement not recognize the Wright brothers as having flown the first airplane, and not Mojaisky as stated in Chap. 3, (p. 18)?

On foot, at a rate of 15-20 miles a day without a break it would take 250-300 days. In practice such a journey could not be completed in a year. High ranking officials sent by the Czar on a mission to Siberia took more than a year with relays of horses to reach such destinations as Iakutsk, Irkutsk or Vladivostock.

But on horseback, changing mounts and covering 100 miles a day, the journey to Vladivostock would take 2 months. This depends of course upon not having to wait for relays, upon the roads being good with no accidents or impassable stretches.

The train takes about 10 days from Vladivostock to Moscow. This is already 30 times faster than on foot. The aeroplane shortens this vast distance even further: A flight of barely 30 hours after leaving the gardens and woods of Moscow and you will see the waves of the Pacific.

But 30 hours is a long time. If we take into account stops on the way for refueling, rest for the passengers and possible delays caused by the weather, the journey will probably take two days.

How pleasant it would be if this time could be reduced to one or two hours! Even if we spend the time on the journey in the train or the plane reading or studying a foreign language the time will be half lost. And man should try and fill every hour of his life to the best of his ability. But for this journey to take 1½ hours is a dream, a chimera. . . .

No, it is not a dream. The space rocket will allow us to shorten distances and really place the whole world at the disposal of man. We do not call them space rockets because they have to travel in space but because in flight they obey the laws of space bodies. They will not

be navigated like aircraft, they will need lift neither by
wings nor propeller to keep them airborne. Let us fly
together on our magic carpet from Moscow to Vladivostock. The date on the calendar is 196. . . .

I do not know in what Moscow suburb the future
office for passengers flying from Moscow to Vladivostock
will be built. Nor by what means of transport we shall
reach the field. Perhaps a modest overhead monorail
which will be run by high frequency current from beneath the road and will pull up in front of a white
building raised on a high silver spire. Helicopters will
probably be used for local travel and one of these will
transport us to the new cosmodrome . . . Now we have
arrived.

In the center of the field, in a vertical position is our
rocket looking like a fantastic obelisk.[9] Let us approach
and examine it in detail. It will certainly be a two
stepped rocket. The broad part which measures about
100 feet in diameter is obviously the booster. The narrow exhausts of its 5 motors are set above a concrete cup
shaped base. This is to prevent the exhaust flames from
damaging or setting light to a large area of the ground
on launching.

A smaller rocket tapers from the booster. It is shorter
than its big brother—about 60 feet long. This has two
exhausts of 3 motors set firmly above a concrete plate.
The motors of this rocket can function even before the
booster has been detached and thus all the motors can
fire simultaneously.

"Firing together," explains the captain, a man in a

[9] "Obelisk" does not seem to be the right term because later it
is given wings.

white uniform with a broad calm face and keen eyes,
"the combined motors will develop a colossal thrust of
more than 850,000 lbs."

"As much as that! . . ." We are amazed.

"That's not excessive," he replies calmly, amused at
our surprise. "The space ships for interplanetary journeys
are equipped with motors which develop a thrust of
several million lbs. I don't mean the ships for long
journeys which run on atomic motors . . . How is it that
you haven't kept up to date with the progress made
during the past ten years?"

Naturally we are not up to date. Our knowledge is
limited. We admit it frankly to the captain. One could
not lie to a man with such an obviously frank and honest
face . . .

"Well, a great many things will be new to you. You
will enjoy many interesting sensations. Incidentally, take
off will be in ten minutes so you had better take your
seat in the passenger cabin."

We enter the light aluminum cabin of the lift which
carries us up to the hatch of the smaller rocket. The
crew are already at their posts.

In the cabin we find comfortable armchairs, circular
ports of dark glass, as we can guess, against solar radiation. In front of us is the television screen. During the
trip we shall be able to watch the latest film or the semi-
final of an international football match.

We sit down in our chairs. How comfortable they are!
But they are comfortable now that the rocket is in a
vertical position. Unless during the flight they assume
a horizontal position we shall fall out of them like peas
shaken from a colander.

The captain reassures us. He advises us to lie back in the chairs until we are almost recumbent. During the flight the chairs will maintain the same gravitational position as they have now, whatever the position of the rocket. They are worked on gyroscopic principles. Perhaps each chair has its own gyroscope or perhaps one central gyroscope works them all,[10] but we have no time to ask the captain, for he is already on the bridge. Two minutes before launching. Tensely we look at the clock: 90 . . . 60 . . . 30 seconds . . . zero. The springs of the chairs sag gently. This is the effect of the acceleration.

The strain does not appear to be excessive. We feel no ill effects. Gradually we can raise our hands, move our heads. Through the glass ports we can see the earth's surface exactly as it appears in the press photographs of rockets. The greater part of the horizon is obscured by the delta wing of our rocket. The sky darkens —so we must be approaching the upper atmosphere. But why can we not hear the drone of the exhausts? Why can we not feel the vibrations? The reply is not immediately forthcoming. After we land the captain will explain that beneath the passengers' cabin are the tanks of the fuel and oxygen which absorb the sound and the vibrations.

We have been airborne for more than 2 minutes. Now the horizon changes and we can surmise that the rocket has suddenly changed position. The booster has been detached. The crew will direct it back to the base. It has completed its task of carrying our rocket up to 15 miles.

The motors continue to fire, but now the sensation of

[10] Why not simple pivots instead of gyros?

"overweight" gradually gives place to a feeling of incredible lightness. Our speed is still less than that of the earth . . .

Now we can no longer see the flames from the exhausts which were visible through the ports. A sense of extraordinary levity . . . it seems as though the rocket were falling into a bottomless abyss. This is the state of weightlessness whose affects on the human body the doctors have discussed at such length. . . .

And in actual fact the rocket is falling, or rather it is flying on its own momentum to a height of more than 300 miles above the earth, in atmosphere so rarefied that it offers practically no resistance. It is flying at a speed of about 3 m/s long the arc of an ellipse of which one focus is the earth. Our ship has taken a leap; it has detached itself from the Earth and is now well on its way to its peak. The distance covered in its flight is in excess of 5,500 miles.

The captain descends the ladder from his bridge. He is still calm but obviously finds it difficult to move about in these conditions of weightlessness. He sits down in a chair. We feel that it would be tactless to ask him about the possibility of an accident.

But he seems to have divined our thoughts for he says:

"There is no greater risk of an accident in our rocket than in an aircraft. It is difficult to imagine what could happen during a flight. Well, suppose that we have miscalculated our power, the rocket would begin to fall and the motors fail. In such a case we jettison the whole rear portion of the rocket including the tanks with their fuel, the pumps and the motors. They fall as dead weight to the Earth and our cabin, transformed into a glider

will return peacefully back to earth on its own wings
. . . It will land like an ordinary glider. . . ."

On the television screen the football match has be-
gun. It is odd to watch colored TV in a state of imponderability in the cabin of a rocket moving at colossal
speed in the ionosphere somewhere between the Urals
and Lake Baikal, 800 miles from our starting point. It
is only odd, of course, because we have not yet become
used to the idea.

A little more than an hour has passed. The captain
has returned to his bridge. The motors are firing again.
By the shift of the horizon we guess that the rocket has
once more changed position. We cannot yet see the out-
lines of Asia wreathed in cloud. The white flames from
the exhausts are now directed ahead. From afar the
ship must look like some monster that has strayed from
the stars, lighting up its path with three gigantic head-
lights.

The acceleration or rather the deceleration—both have
the same effect on the human body—increases, but the
strain is no greater than it was on launching. It represented about 100 ft. p.s.—3g. A healthy person can com-
fortably withstand this.

And now, at last, a slight jolt and the rocket speeds
like an ordinary plane but with the exhausts in front
along the concrete runway of the cosmodrome. It comes
to a standstill. The door of the cabin opens and we descend. We could be back in Moscow—the same white
buildings, the same offices, the same colored umbrellas
of the restaurant on the roof of the 4th floor and the
aerials of the radiotele control; a flag is flying at the
masthead on top of this gleaming obelisk. But it is not
Moscow: we have arrived at Vladivostock. The whole

flight has lasted just over an hour. After completing their business people can return to Moscow by the evening rocket.

These rocket communications between points far distant on the globe, at distances of 2,500 or 10,000 miles are not fantasy; this is the next stage in rocket development which science will have to achieve.

The Birth of a Second Moon

Since the days of Galileo, when men discovered that satellites of certain planets existed, the question has often been asked whether the Moon is our only satellite. More than once news has been publishd of the discovery of a second satellite barely visible to the naked eye and difficult to distinguish with a telescope on account of its small size. But these reports have always been subsequently contradicted. So far a second satellite has not been discovered.

In all probability the Earth has not and will not have another "natural" satellite of noteworthy dimensions. But now it has definitely been given an artificial satellite. And in future it will have not one but many, built for various purposes and of various sizes, moving along different orbits at different distances from the Earth.

There will be enormous artificial satellites—whole space cities with their greenhouses, helio-electric stations, observatories and perhaps restaurants and hotels for passengers in transit. There will be modest baby satellites weighing a few lbs. launched by scientists with special equipment to discover some secret of space. Naturally the first earth satellite, could not be a gigantic space station; it was a tiny automatic explorer, our sputnik. The present stage of scientific development made it possible to create a satellite of this nature.

Recently with a roar of its exhausts a gigantic rocket 120 ft. high and more than 30 feet broad flew up into the blue sky. At the start its ascent was slow like all rockets at their launching. But when its motors got into full action it sped into the sky until it was no more than an invisible dot.

Let us follow our rocket. Now all the propellant for the first stage has been consumed by the voracious motors. The booster is immediately detached automatically. By its momentum it still continues to rise: but how rapidly the second section of the rocket leaves it behind in the rarefied air.

After losing its momentum, braked by the air resistance, the booster remains stationary for a moment before stalling and starting to dive.

The second step of the rocket is by this time many hundreds of miles away. This second rocket speeds ever higher, the power of its exhausts having received an increase of speed from its booster. What speed did it reach? Normally the altitude attainable by two stepped rockets does not much exceed 250 miles. Therefore it had to climb another 60 miles.

But how did it succeed? The exhausts which so far had pointed vertically downwards canted and the rocket levelled out on to a course parallel to the earth's surface. The exhausts were now horizontal. Did the rocket turn automatically? Was it controlled from the earth?

At the same time the rocket flying at a height of 200 miles above the earth underwent a second transformation at great speed. Now we can divulge that the rocket did not consist of two but of three sections. These separated. The second, now empty, moved slowly, losing height, along a very flat trajectory. But the third, continually increasing its speed, flew like a meteor. When the last drop of propellant had left its tanks in the form of burning gas in the ionosphere, the rocket had attained the speed of 25,500 ft./s—circular velocity. We have already stated that a rocket travelling at circular velocity along a certain orbit continually loses height without ever being able to dive. Obviously this was to be the fate of the small remnant, not unlike the tip of a pencil, of the powerful three stepped rocket.

But apparently our rocket had not yet undergone all its tranformations. Flying at an almost inconceivable speed, hurtling round the earth at what we call circular velocity the third segment of the rocket suddenly split in two. Inside was a tiny sphere of gleaming aluminum and plastic.

This sphere was the first artificial satellite of our planet—the Sputnik, the second moon whose glorious birth we were privileged to attend.

The Automatic Laboratory in the Sputnik

At a distance of 200 miles from the earth, the atmosphere is so rarefied that a body travelling at high speed meets with hardly any air resistance. We have purposely said "hardly any," for there is a certain resistance all the same. As soon as the aluminum sphere of our artificial moon leaped from the open half of the rocket it started to outstrip it. Evidently its perfect aerodynamic form was better and the resistance it met was less than that encountered by the rest of the rocket. But for a comparatively long time they travelled forward close together.

The speed of our artificial moon is stupendous: we have already given its speed at 25,500 ft./s, in other words about 17 m/s. Thus it circles the globe in less than an hour and a half. In 24 hours this moon rises and sets 16 times. Morning and evening, lit by the rays of the sun, it is visible through binoculars or a small telescope. In the blue sky at twilight the first space body created by the brains and hands of men can actually be seen. Let us meet the "inhabitants" of this artificial satellite and see what purpose they serve.

Our artificial moon is a hollow aluminum sphere with a diameter of rather more than 18 inches. Including the insrtuments carried it weighs a little more than 100 lbs. Most of this weight is made up by the scientific instruments.[11]

The sputnik circles the earth on a peculiar trajectory: it crosses the two poles so that during the first days of its flight it should not be eclipsed by the earth. The new moon will never for one instant enter the Earth's shadow:[12] it slips into the morning and evening twilight, constantly illuminated by the sun.

This is no coincidence and is due to two circumstances. One of the most important tasks of the Sputnik is to study solar radiation. Secondly, the energy of the sun furnishes the energy to work the instruments it carries.

The Sputnik revolves at great speed on its own axis.

[11] Radio Moscow reported that Sputnik I weighed over 183 pounds and was nearly 23 inches in diameter.

[12] Sputnik I was not on a polar orbit. It was eclipsed by the earth.

It was given this rotation on earth before the launching. In addition it is equipped with a number of small protuberances placed to exploit the least air resistance.

Nor was it a coincidence that the first artificial satellite was given a shape conforming to the heavenly bodies created by nature. This guarantees it stability of position, ensuring that it will always turn the same side or rather the same pole to the Sun, for our dwarf Satellite has two poles. . . .

The whole part of the satellite turned towards the sun has a skin of plastic material to concentrate the solar rays on a photo-electric battery which produces the electric current.[13] This current charges tiny accumulators which feed all the instruments in the Sputnik. This is the nature of the helio-electric station, the beating heart of the satellite.

There are two windows in this plastic skin. One is a quartz lens which allows the passage of ultra-violet rays. The apparatus which captures and records their total intensity and studies their spectrum is installed behind this window.

The second is made of beryllium. What rays could pass through a plate of metal possessing such a high degree of impenetrability? Only X rays. This appartus therefore is designed to record the X rays sent out by the sun.

Another window is to be seen on the Sputnik's equator. This produces a smoke screen—a cloud of sodium vapor to mark the position of the satellite in the sky.[14] Centrifugal force disperses the sodium gas which

[13] If a solar battery were used, why did the signals from the satellite cease after only two weeks?
[14] Sodium vapor was not reported seen by Western observers.

leaves this aperture; the little cloud, illuminated by the sun, will be easily visible from the earth.

If we were to open the lid of our Sputnik we should be amazed at the quantity and diversity of the instruments inside. We should find gamma and cosmic counters, instruments to study the radiation of the Aurora Borealis, to calculate electrons and a magnetometer to investigate the earth's magnetic field. Near the pole opposite the sunlight side is the nexus of the communicating system.

An aluminum spigot is inserted in this pole, making the satellite look like a toffee apple. This serves as an aerial. The Sputnik has to maintain constant communication with the earth, otherwise there would be no reason for its existence.

The research instruments inside the satellite continually record data. These are registered in code by a system of radio signals and passed to the transmitter. The instruments record continuously but the transmitter functions periodically at 45 minute intervals.[15] The total data given is transmitted to the earth in a brief period of 30 seconds. The transmission time has to be limited because of a great expenditure of energy which can only be recuperated very slowly. If the radio were kept switched on all the time, the accumulators would become exhausted and the instruments would cease to work.

This is the external and internal structure of the extra-terrestrial laboratory which is precisely what our Sputnik is.

We do not know in advance how long the Sputnik

[15] Pulse of each signal, operating on 40.002 mc and 20.005 mc, was 0.3 seconds. It is doubtful that a third transmission was used. Such a transmission was not reported by Western observers.

will continue to be a satellite. Although air resistance is negligible, it will gradually lose its impetus. It will gradually decrease and it will descend lower and lower into ever denser atmosphere. Finally becoming red hot from the friction of the air it will burn like a meteor in the night sky.

After Sputnik II, other moons will be launched to explore the upper atmosphere and the regions of space nearest to the earth. A great variety of tasks will fall upon these new moons. From now on it will be possible to build artificial satellites of various sizes and weights.

Some will merely investigate the directions of the air currents, the degrees of ionization and the other phenomena in the upper ionosphere, for example their influence on the climate. The meteorologists will watch the signals from these moons: their findings will enable them to give long-term weather forecasts.

Other artificial moons acting in the extreme upper regions like giant stream-lined tubes will deal with aerodynamic questions, highly rarified braking in conditions and supersonic speeds. The designers of the future space ships will be particularly interested in the results of these researches. As we have already shown it is of great importance to them to ensure the braking of the space ship on its entrance into the upper atmosphere. Upon the result of such researches will depend the success of space travel.

The biologists will transform the satellite into a greenhouse.[16] For them the important thing to know is the influence of certain components of space radiations on plant life and seeds, on plant development and what measures they will have to take to obtain the maximum

[16] For the biologists to do their work, they will need recoverable satellites. Therefore, re-entry and capture problems must be solved.

the instruments for observation, the helio-electric plants for charging the accumulators and the transmitting set for contact with the earth, there will be oxygen tanks for his breathing apparatus to absorb the carbon dioxide.[18] A protective shield against direct action of cosmic rays, a minimum supply of food and water—all this will be installed for the comfort of the man. Sputnik II, which carried the dog Laika, conformed to these principles.

As was foreseen, the first artificial satellite, Sputnik I, fell at the end of its term on a circular orbit and burnt as it entered the atmosphere. It could naturally have been salvaged, but it was not worthwhile.[19] To equip it with the necessary retarding mechanism and to allow it to descend slowly through the atmosphere would have meant sacrificing part of the instruments and increasing the weight.

It would of course have been a fine thing to preserve it in a muesum—man's first created planet; but it would have been too costly and we renounced the opportunity.

But what will happen in the case of the first manned satellite which will have to return to earth?

It will have to be given retractable wings so that it can be maneuvred in the upper atmosphere until its speed has gradually been reduced. It will also have to be provided with a parachute which will brake it even more when it penetrates the lower atmosphere. It may have to be given retarding rockets in the nose, which will mean an increase in the supply of fuel.

[18] Oxygen will not absorb carbon dioxide. Probably, the author means lithium hydroxide.

[19] Doubtful that the USSR could have salvaged their satellite— they certainly would have wanted to because it would have been just as big a feat as the launching.

The problem is still being studied. Braking in the atmosphere is not as simple as it might appear. Meteors which enter the atmosphere burn up entirely. Eye witness accounts of the V2 show that during its fall over London it gave off a faint reddish glow. The space rocket heats to a temperature of 700° in the atmosphere. To reduce this temperature by braking, the duration of its flight will have to be prolonged. Nor is this an easy matter.

Only after future experimental and theoretical aero-dynamic researches into the results of high speeds in rarefied gases will it be possible to make the necessary decisions.

Island in Space

Rockets will launch their artificial moons ever higher; they will increase in size and passenger accommodation will be improved. Finally, some thousand miles beyond the confines of the Earth will begin the construction of an "eternal" satellite. Eternal, because unless its designers decide otherwise it will never leave its orbit and will continue to revolve for ever round the Earth.

The Soviet engineer, B. Liapunov has put forward a plan for an inhabited satellite. This is to be assembled in space from the skeletons of rockets launched into its orbit. The first space builders in special suits adapted to the needs of their work will weld it from the fragments of these rockets which will be flying at an enormous speed in relation to the Earth but at insignificant speed in space. Doubtless this satellite will be assembled with entirely new methods still unknown on Earth. Concave mirrors and thin lenses which concentrate the rays of the sun on one point will be the tools of the space welders. What beautiful, bright weldings of unoxydized metal devoid of the slightest air bubble will be possible in space!

The workers will probably be attached to the satellite in construction by flexible but stout nylon lines. They will not feel the weight of these "chains" which will prevent the astronaut from being gradually carried away into space. A clumsy turn or a false movement would result in a sudden burst of speed. After a few minutes a man, unless he were secured to the satellite, would be transformed into a tiny star which would move rapidly away. And then try and find him in the void!

The builders will of course be provided with portable rockets to enable them to move about in space. Their suits will carry walkie-talkie sets for communication with the mother ship. The soles of their boots will be fitted with magnets so that they can walk about on the steel parts of the ship—although little of this heavy metal will be used.[20] But the nylon lines will be indispensable.

Rockets despatched from the earth will be the sole component parts of the future island in space. The ring-shaped construction will be given a rotating movement to provide artificial gravity.

Not a fragment of metal or substance will be wasted. From the very start the satellite will be provided with its own energy—the helio-electric plant. Its mirrors will be the metal skins of the rockets arranged in sectional lengths in the shape of a parabola. The inner surfaces

[20] Why use magnets if there is little steel present?

of these rocket mirrors will be accurately fashioned on Earth.

In the heart of the helio-electric plant will be a steam boiler—a copper tube with a water cooling jacket. This boiler will have direct flow: passing along the inside of the mirror, the water will evaporate completely. The steam at high pressure will pass into a steam turbine in the shade of the mirror and from there into a spiral tube—the condenser. In this way the desired coolant will be produced in this condenser which expels the heat direct into space which has a temperature approaching absolute zero.[21] The size of the condenser will be calculated to maintain a temperature of about 4° above zero and a pressure of some hundredths of atmospheric pressure.

The condensed water will be returned to the boiler by a common pump working at high pressure off the shaft of the steam turbine. The cycle will be repeated ad infinitum. The water collects the heat of the sun's rays and returns it to the blades of the turbine before receiving more heat.

It is conceivable that the heat conductor used by the space steam turbine will not be water. Scientists will have discovered a body capable of exploiting the immense difference in temperature between the boiler run by concentrated solar radiation and the condenser in the shade, based in the freezing cold of outer space. The

[21] The boiler would have to be located at the mirror's focus, not "inside of the mirror." Also, there is no conduction or convection of heat into space, therefore cooling plan would be of dubious value, depending, as it were, only on heat radiation. Also, why not use the solar energy in a direct conversion to electricity, via solar cells, and avoid complications?

minimum temperature which can be used for water is too high, −0°.

The shaft of an electric generator is connected to the shaft of the steam turbine. The current produced will be at the disposal of the space builders. The helio-electric plant will be suspended in space with sufficient stability. It will be given this stability by the rotor of the steam turbine and by the electric generator—a kind of powerful gyroscope.

An interesting detail will be observed in this aggregated turbine rotor. It will not always rotate in the same direction. The shaft of the rotor will be divided into two segments with an identical momentum and opposite rotation. Unless the designers used this method the whole helio-electric plant would be given a rotatory movement —in fact it would have no base from which it could transmit the moment of reaction such as occurs with steam turbines on earth.

Naturally the entire parts of the space electric power station: turbines, electric generators and refrigerator, will be built on Earth and assembled in space. After this a giant telescope will be mounted. Its mirror, many feet in diameter, will be made of light metal. Astronomers are convinced that its form will not differ from those in use on Earth. But since there is no gravity in space it will have to be turned with the tumost caution otherwise it will cant by the force of inertia. For this reason the gleaming paraboloid space telescope will be given rigid metal ribs on the convex side.

Even greater will be the dimensions of the radiotelescope. Its network of flexible and elastic wire will cover an area of several thousand square miles.

The astronomers and physicists will already begin to draw up the schedule of their scientific work before the builders have completed the essentials of the space island. Every few hours transport rockets will be despatched from the Earth. Their bodies will be welded into a new ring. At the same time the component parts of the spacedrome and the greenhouse will be sent up. In the center of the island will be a huge arena. The rocket passengers will land on this arena, the axis of which will be kept rigorously in the same direction. In the walls of this fortress will be built a series of huge hangars several hundred yards long to house space ships. They will serve as supply bases.

The remains of the space within the island ring will be occupied in the greenhouse. Its "lower" base will be made of the remains of rocket skins, while the upper story turned to the sun will be covered with a roof of transparent plastic material perhaps 250 yards in diameter. Calculations for the durability of this roof will give the designers a lot of headaches. The air pressure in the greenhouse will be maintained far below that of the atmosphere and as a result the pressure of its total area will be colossal. For increased solidity, the framework of the transparent walls will be joined to the base of the greenhouse with hollow metal supports.

On its completion a luxuriant vegetation will grow. The sudden changes of living conditions will probably result in a radical change in the plant forms. The space gardeners imagine that they will be able to grow fruits of a size and nutritive value quite unknown on Earth.

But this will be in the far future. The designers of

the first space island will above all concentrate on the quality of the welding. They will have to ensure that the joints are airtight. Otherwise it would be catastrophic for the inhabitants of the island.

And finally the last stages of the montage will begin. Rockets will begin to carry fuel instead of assembly parts. The island will then be transformed into an enormous supply base.

The ships which carry this fuel will not be broken up and used as material but will return to earth. Each one will make a dozen journeys before being broken up and incorporated in the general building as one of its giant tanks.

In the space drome—the huge central arena of the island—the assembling of the ships for long interplanetary journeys will start.

Transport Trains

One of the creators of the V2 rocket, Wernher von Braun has published his plan for a three-stepped rocket which, according to him, will ensure communication with the artificial satellite under construction. The total height of these rocket stages will be 270 ft.; at its base the rocket will have a diameter of 70 ft. and the total weight will amount to about 6,400 tons. In this way the space ship on launching will be the size of a small cruiser.

The fuel used will be nitric acid and hydrazene as oxidizer, injected into the combustion chambers by high performance pumps. This oxidizer is the most powerful yet known and therefore the most suitable for space rockets.[22]

The pumps will be driven by turbines running on peroxide of hydrogen. Thus in addition to its load of oxidizer the rocket will have to carry tanks of this fuel.

In the lower booster there will be 39 basic and 12 steering motors. The total thrust of these motors will be 12,800 tons and at the launching they will exceed the weight of the space ship. 4,800 tons of fuel will be burnt in 84 seconds, representing 75½ of the total weight of the rocket. The first step, when emptied, will be detached and descend to earth on a parachute. The motors of the second step will then go into action—22 basic and 12 steering motors. As soon as this second booster has exhausted its fuel, it too will descend to earth by parachute.

The boosters will therefore not be destroyed but used again on further launchings. To effect these parachute descents and to reduce landing speed powder rockets will be used.

The third step of the rocket will only have 5 liquid propellant rockets. In its nose will be the passenger accommodation, the payload, the steering mechanism and the charthouse. Two pairs of delta wings with elevators and ailerons will allow a gliding descent to the Earth.

Multiple stepped rockets have also been designed for communication with the satellite. An interesting design for a transport rocket of this type was presented at the

[22] Nitric acid as the oxidizer and hydrazine as the fuel. Even so, the last statement in this paragraph is not true, for even oxygen is a better oxidizer than nitric acid.

9th Congress of the American Society of Astronautics.

According to this plan the communication rocket—also called the freighter—is a three-stepped type. Each section has retractable wings and its own pilot. The total height of this rocket is 275 ft. and its overall weight is 9,000 tons of which 7,800 consist of propellant. The third and final step, which will reach the satellite's orbit 500 miles above the earth together with the crew weighs 35 tons.

The first huge booster will raise the rocket to 25 miles giving it a speed of 235 m.p.h. On detaching, it will descend like a glider to about 300 miles from the launching site.

The second booster will carry the "freighter" to a height of 40 miles; this will also become detached and glide to 1,000 miles from the launching site.

Now the rockets of the third step go into action. They will carry it to the satellite's position. After unloading its cargo and passengers it will return to its point of departure.

The multiple rocket is designed to carry out more than one trip. The first and second sections after landing will fly back to their base. The wings contain jet or piston engines with their own fuel tanks and they will return to base like normal aircraft with their own pilot and crew. There they will be attached to another supply rocket, refuelled, and take off once more for the satellite.

The third step, having reached circular velocity, will be incorporated in the construction of the satellite island ring.

Similar plans exist in many other combines. All of which goes to prove that the idea of creating a huge earth satellite is no chimera but a real and feasible project in the light of modern science.

A Laboratory in Space

Space . . . but it is the void! No, it is nothing of the sort. Why do you hanker after this space? Is it not better to stay on earth?

This is how badly informed people reason.

But we are here to explain what will allow us to conquer space.

To begin with space is not the void. It contains—even if in rarefied form—clouds of dust and gas. Furthermore it is pierced by solar and stellar radiation, by electric and magnetic gravitational fields.

The first to fly in it will be the scientists. They are attracted by the exceptional conditions they will be able to create as a result of their observations.

The first of these is imponderability. Biologists will experiment with animals and plants; metallurgists will study the crystal structure of metals outside the force of gravity, and physicists the reciprocal action of weightless masses for example of gases and liquids.

Cosmic rays: scientists have installed instruments weighing many tons for the study of cosmic rays on the tops of the highest mountains. Sounding balloons and rockets have been sent up to considerable heights. But no scientist so far has been able to study these cosmic rays in their natural surroundings before being deflected by the atmosphere. The solution of the problem of these rays will advance our knowledge of the nature of elementary particles. Only in space will they be able to study cosmic rays in their primordial state.

The Sun: its activity is too essential on earth for the secrets of its radiation not to be of major interest. The spectrum which filters through the atmosphere is only a makeshift. To study the complete spectrum, its mutations and their influence on the climate, on magnetic storms and the movements of the atmosphere can succeed in an extra-terrestrial laboratory.

The work of the astronomers on Earth is perforce a very haphazard affair. It is hampered above all by the opacity of the air as a result of various radiations. If these rays could reach the bottom of the "atmospheric ocean" the astronomers would force them to reveal a great deal about the universe. Moreover, the constant atmospheric disturbances impede their work; the solar disc visible in their telescopes quivers and is deformed, losing its clarity. The astronomer, too, must have an observatory in space. How much he will discover as soon as the obstacle of the atmosphere has been removed!

The temperature: in the scientists' laboratories costly and complicated machinery which demands great power functions round the clock to create in a small volume a temperature approaching absolute zero. The tubes are encased in a thick layer of ice; the walls of glass and metal exude a frost of $-100°$ and, finally, there emerge the first drops of a light transparent liquid—liquefied helium or hydrogen. To obtain lower temperatures is increasingly difficult. Only for a few seconds can a temperature equivalent to a few degree above absolute zero be reproduced.

The temperature in outer space—a laboratory of unlimited dimensions—is only 4° above absolute zero. All that is required to obtain this temperature is protection from the sun's rays by a series of screens. What new mysteries will the physicist who has such low temperatures at his disposal be able to unveil?

On the other hand, by concentrating the solar rays through a lens of a concave mirror he will be able to obtain a temperature of several thousand degrees. The possibility of such contrasts in temperature is another important asset for the research worker.

But is this space station really so vital for the scientists? So that another of those weighty tomes filled with figures incomprehensible to the layman may appear?

Yes. It will be the scientists who conquer space. They have always been the pioneers of the unknown. They were the first to ascend in balloons and to them we owe the benefits of aviation. They were the first to experiment with certain substances and to them we owe the fact that we can wear silk, a material at one time only available to kings. It was the scientists who first wound wires round a bobbin so that in our own rooms we can now see and hear the whole world on our radio and television sets.

The latest discovery—coded in abstruse, mathematical formulae and special symbols, which at first sight seem so bewildering—will tomorrow give a drive to the development of science, bestowing new benefits on mankind and rendering our lives fuller and brighter.

Scientific interests alone demand the creation of a laboratory in space on an artificial satellite; it will show a great return. It is not only the interests of today but of the future that make him brave the dangers.

The atmosphere of the earth at the bottom of which we live, extends to a height of more than 60 miles. It appears to be a single entity. What falls into its upper strata has direct consequences on those below. How greatly the weather forecasts will improve when meteorologists will be able to observe the conditions of the upper strata from a satellite. The importance of these weather forecasts for communications, agriculture and building is obvious.

In the earth's atmosphere today we find not only high performance rockets but aircraft carrying passengers, mail and freight. From year to year their speeds increase and at the same time the air resistance they meet in flight. The time will come when the huge increase in engine power and the consumption of huge quantities of fuel will not give a corresponding increase in speed. The air resistance will absorb any such increase.

"We have overcome the sound barrier," say the scientists, "What is the way out? How can we progress any further?"

At a height of 3 miles the density of the air is 1.6 times less than at sea level and at a height of 15 miles 15.6 times less! But even there the resistance is still very strong. Thus we shall have to wait for any notable increase in speed until we fly in the ionosphere. But this can only take place after the conditions ruling there have been studied. The ionosphere, on the other hand, is only the antechamber of space. The artificial satellite offers the greatest opportunity for studying it.

From space we could see at one time half the globe. This is important not only for meteorologists who observe the shifting masses of cloud. The television experts maintain that if they could set up on a satellite a tele-radio transmitting station they could guarantee perfect reception over one half of the world. Is this not an intriguing prospect?

Space is an inexhaustible source of energy taken, one might say, directly from the sun. According to the scientists, we may perhaps move out into space solely for practical purposes, for power and the construction of helio-electric stations.

But the organization of a laboratory in space is the first step towards conquering the other planets.

Chapter Seven

THE ASSAULT ON THE MOON

Preliminary Reconnaissance

NATURALLY, none of the countless artificial moons could take the place of our satellite which has been there since time immemorial and to which the human race has grown accustomed. We shall not even see most of the small artificial moons of short duration which will fly at an immense speed round the earth. But who can ignore the presence of the moon?

The moon will probably be the first celestial body upon which man will set foot. But before this, his notions of the moon will have been much enriched thanks to teleguided rockets.

It is not easy, today, to describe the details of such a rocket. It will probably leave the earth as a multiple-stage rocket. If we succeeded in launching it from a satellite the problem would be entirely different. But we can already imagine how problems will be solved with its aid. Let us take a look at the controls of the first space ship launched to explore the moon.

. . . In a large dark room where the glass and nickel of the control switches and instrument panels gleam on the walls, small colored lights flash on luminous hands, oscillate on the dials, a group of scientists stands before a huge television screen.

The screen which quivers and shudders is almost black. Here and there points of light appear on it. In the center is suspended a cigar shaped object lit up only on one side.

On this television screen we shall see all that could be seen in a telescope following the progress of the first space ship to the moon. The small cigar in the center is the 200 ft. long ship on its headlong flight through space.

Below the large screen is the small screen of the oscillograph. On it a green line vibrates in sharp zigzags. This is the radar communication. The beam accompanies the ship throughout its journey; it contacts the speedcraft and as though reassured that all is well, returns to the earth. Here, transformed into a fluorescent zigzag on the screen, it reports to the scientists that everything is in order aboard. The data of its position are immediately worked out by electronic machines and thus its course, speed and position are constantly known.

The men in the control room also know the readings of all the instruments in the ship itself. It carries a recording apparatus and a transmitter. The rocket has already covered half its course. It is approaching the moon; on the screen has appared the gentle sickle of our satellite the moon in its first phase.

The scientists compare their calculations with the information furnished by the instruments and give the ship the appropriate directions. Suddenly streaks appear on the screen—the exhausts of the retarding rockets. The cigar turns slowly on a different course. Now on earth it is seen from a completely different angle. The exhaust lines disappear; the motors have been cut out. The instruments report to the watchers that the rocket has become a satellite of the moon. It is now moving along a circular orbit. At this moment they will be able to see the other side of the moon which has never been seen before by man and has always been a matter of conjecture. What a pity that the passengers of the rocket in this unprecedented flight are only automatic machines and teleguided mechanisms.

Now the screen is suddenly transformed. The tremulous shadows are replaced by a colored contour picture of the moon's surface seen in close up. With astounding clarity a huge oval circle appears: the Sea of Disaster. From the earth it is impossible to see its colors even through the most powerful telescope. Now it shows up green on the colored screen. The scientists recognize the craters and circles which they have christened: Cleomedes, Gemini, Langrin. . . .

Near this zone, which has been half explored by telescope lie those parts of the planet invisible from the earth. New craters, new mountain chains, brownish rocks and ocean beds. The men watching, forgetting for the moment that everything will be recorded on the film take out their pencils and draw rapid sketches . . . Excitement is at its peak.

By this time the reader will have guessed that this is a colored transmission from the space ship.

But suddenly a shadow crosses the screen obliterating the picture. It trembles for an instant, fades and disappears.

A breakdown? An imperfection of the set or a fault in the reception? No, there is no cause for alarm. It is a phenomenon quite common in the solar system—an eclipse of the satellite. Our ship is now hidden behind the moon; the huge body of the moon has placed itself like a gigantic screen between us and the radio waves so that they will no longer reach the earth. But this is the first eclipse of an artificial satellite recorded in history! The first case in our billion year existence![1]

After a rigorously calculated time the ship reappears on the opposite side, from the dark side of the moon. Now the watchers will see its passage across the illuminated disc. Perhaps on their orders a message will be sent to the moon—a shell whose explosion will be visible on earth. The ship will make several orbits round the moon, 20-60 miles abve its surface, gradually changing its direction of flight so that the largest area can be observed. At a predetermined moment the order will be given for it to return to earth. The artificial moon satellite will become a space ship once more.

And finally the wanderer will return. The scientists will develop the film, decipher the data given by the instruments. In the world press photos will appear of

[1] Earth is about 3-billion years old; man has been here about a million of them.

the invisible side of the moon taken by the cine camera.
It will be one more step towards the conquest of the
universe.

The Automatic Tank

The Soviet Scientists, Professor J. Hlebzevich considers the first trip to the moon will be made by a rocket
carrying automatic instruments instead of men. At each
stage of the assault on space man will entrust his ex-
plorations to robots. We already know what a gigantic
task it will be to send a maned ship to the moon, to
ensure that they arrive there alive and can return to
earth. The weight of this rocket on landing on the moon
would be scores of tons. What an enormous weight it
would have to be on its launching!

According to Hlebzevich, an automatic laboratory capable of giving a host of important data would only weigh
a few hundred pounds—not much more than the light
utility car, the Moskvich. It need never return to the
earth and could continue to fly for ever round the moon.
Furthermore the instrument room would not be affected
by acceleration and need not be airtight. Special trans-
mitters have been used in certain projectiles and function perfectly after the gun has been fired. The aboli-
tion of g strain will facilitate the task of launching a
rocket equipped as a scientific laboratory to the moon.

This is how the above mentioned scientist envisages
the work of such a mobile laboratory.

The rocket, radar controlled from earth, will approach the moon. Now it nears the surface of our satellite which is covered with a thick layer of porous dust

rocks and mineral fragments. The automatic instruments controlled from Earth turn the rocket and the retarding exhaust motors in the nose go into action. Burning the last drops of fuel the rocket brakes its fall and descends slowly on to the moon.

Chips of rock are blown into the air but they settle immediately since there is no atmosphere on the moon to keep them in the air. The base of the rocket on impact with the soil is half buried in the friable dust and irreparably bent. The fuel tanks are broken. Only the nose of the rocket has remained undamaged.

This crash was foreseen. The body and the fuel tanks were built to take the shock of landing and preserve the rocket's brain.

A window opens in the upper part and a small armored car with caterpillar tracks descends. It slowly descends on to the moon's surface—slowly according to our concepts, for the moon's attraction is 6 times smaller than that of the earth and thus the rate of fall will be six times slower.

But having touched the ground, the armored car will pitch and use its tracks. Its shape is such that as it falls it will return to its normal position like a rebounding toy. Actually it has two normal positions: it will also function "with its legs in the air" and as a result of its tracks it will, on occasions, be upside down.

Now the instruments emerge from its body. A flexible skeleton ejects the transmitting and receiving aerials. Now the complicated sensory organs of the armored car are raised—the tele eye—the television receiving camera. This can turn in all directions, scrutinize the horizon, and look ahead as though to see where "to place its feet." Every sensation experienced by this apparatus is

immediately transmitted back to Earth. The watchers
will see on the screen of their televisor as clearly as
though they themselves were sitting in the armored car.

On an order from Earth the telereceiver will turn in
various directions, choosing the easiest path, and finally
the car moves off. It is looking for a spot for its first
series of observations.

Its body houses various instruments for investigating
conditions reigning on the moon; temperature, composition of the soil, etc. But this is not all; it also carries
equipment to gather samples of the soil to a depth of
several feet. It is essential to know the specific weight of
the dusty soil—the layer of crushed rocks of which the
moon's surface was originally composed. These data are
necessary before a manner rocket can land.

Imagine yourself navigating a space ship which is to
land on earth without knowing the physical conditions
reigning there. You would naturally try to land on terra
firma. Ahead you see the boundless forests of Siberia.
You choose a huge bare patch—an ideal spacedrome . . .
and you sink into a morass.

On the earth's surface there are quicksands in the
deserts which would engulf any heavy object which fell
in them. A landing on such a spot would mean certain
death. It will be one of the tasks of the armored car to
choose the landing site for the eventual manned rocket.
It will have to be flat with a sufficiently hard surface
without deep cracks.

. . . Leaving on the thick layer of soft dust the trace
of its broad tracks, the car sets out in search of a site for
the first lunar spacedrome.

How long will the car work on the moon? This depends on the engines which also feed the instruments

with electric current. They will be engines burning fuel brought from the Earth. Taking into account the reduced gravity, the stock of fuel may last only a few days or at best a few weeks. But it may have supplementary motors and accumulators which can be recharged not once but several times on the spot. The same inexhaustible source of energy will do this—the sun which will also run the helio-electric station on the artificial satellite. Actually the conditions of solar radiation on the moon differ little from the radiation in outer space.

Possibly the supply of energy will be insufficient to run all the mechanisms and instruments in the armored car during the long lunar night which lasts 14 days. During this time a renewal of energy will be impossible. But at dawn as soon as the accumulators are slightly recharged by the electrogenerators which are self started, the instruments will be given a new lease of life and start to transmit to Earth the results of their observations, then to trail across the expanses of lunar seas. This will be rehearsed many times so that the instruments will not break down from some unforeseen causes or be put out of action.

From the Artificial Satellite

The space ship built to reach the moon from the artificial satellite will differ very much from the rockets despatched from the earth, which we have just discussed.

The winner of the first international prize for the encouragement of astronautics, the Soviet scientist A. Sternfeld has published his first full scale plan for such a ship to be assembled on the artificial satellite from where it would be launched to fly round the moon and return to Earth.

A space ship launched from the satellite will not have to overcome the resistance of a dense layer of air to be met like one being launched from the earth. Thus it will not have to be streamlined—aerodynamic demands do not exist in space. The outward form will be determined by other considerations.

The launching speed would be far lower than a launching from the earth because the satellite itself would already be travelling at a great speed. This would have to be increased by about 12,500 ft./s for the ship to take its place in the moon's orbit. It could be given this without the great acceleration needed to leave the earth. In other words a very powerful motor would be unnecessary.

The construction of this ship would depend upon its destination. One designed to fly round the moon and return to earth would differ from one made to land on the moon. The rocket for a flight to Mars will bear no resemblance to the "moon rockets"—they will be streamlined because Mars has an atmosphere.

Let us consider the design of a circumlunar rocket with return to Earth. We will decide upon its parts and we then see how they can be assembled rationally.

On leaving the artificial satellite it must develop an additional speed of nearly 2 miles/s. This will require an appreciable amount of fuel. Our first requirement therefore is two large fuel tanks—one for the oxidizer and one for the propellant. Then we must have an exhaust rocket motor—a small liquid propellant motor.

On its arrival at the moon it will have to decelerate.

Deceleration can be quite moderate—a few hundred ft./s —but this will also consume fuel. Our third requirement will be two small tanks of oxidizer to transform the ship into an artificial moon satellite.

After a few flights round the moon, the ship will have to start on its homeward voyage to the Earth. It will now need about the same quantity of fuel as it did on becoming a moon satellite. So fourthly, we must add two more small tanks.

The braking on earth is done in relation to the earth's atmosphere. This time we shall need no fuel, but it is obvious that we shall need special, retractable wings and a hermetically sealed streamlined cabin. Thus the fifth essential is a glider for landing on earth.

The cabin of such a glider is not large. It is difficult enough to work in for any length of time so it would not be a suitable permanent abode for the astronauts. Possibly we shall have to attach to the rocket an empty tank for the use of the crew as a laboratory.

Admittedly this is possible but there is a far simpler solution. Why not utilize as living quarters the large tanks which will empty a few minutes after take off from the artificial satellite? The crew could spend the first anxious moments in the narrow cabin of the glider.

So the great tanks will be adapted to the living requirements of the crew during the whole period of the voyage. These together with the glider cabin will constitute the central nucleus of the space ship.

They will have to be arranged so that the crew has easy access from the cabin to the empty tanks.

The small tanks of fuel which will be consumed on the transformation into a moon satellite will not be needed after that moment. It is pointless returning with them to Earth; it will be better to detach them and let them fly for ever round the moon. It would be possible to install automatic devices with a miniature helio-electric station so that they could transmit their information for ever. There will eventually be great numbers of these meteorological stations which will report the weather in outer space. If we have decided to jettison these tanks on the way it will be necessary to attach them to the end of rockets. The second pair of small tanks for the return to earth will only be emptied once the course is set. It will not be necessary to detach them.

Now let us try to systemize things. So in the center—the large fuel tanks and the annex to the glider cabin. To the tail of the glider we shall attach the two small tanks which are to be jettisoned en route. On the other hand, we shall place the second pair with which we return to earth next to the large tanks. Behind these the rocket motors.

This system has been adopted for a good reason. The axis of the exhaust rockets must pass through the ship's center of gravity, otherwise it will turn on its own axis in space as a ship will spin if only one of its screws is turning. The easiest way of obtaining this coincidence of direction is by aligning all the elements of our ship very symmetrically along one axis.

What will be the shape of the tanks?

Probably the shape which will give maximum volume for a minimum of space—in other words spherical. For the large tanks we shall use the ones which have reached the artificial satellite from the earth. These in all probability will be cylindrical; they will have to be adopted to the streamlined form of earth launched rockets.

The joints of our space ship will not need to be par-

ticularly solid; they will only have to withstand the
force of inertia on take off. Where fixed parts are
needed, welding will be adequate. For movable parts,
tubes filled with explosive will do; to free them from the
rocket they can be exploded by means of electric current.
This can be done without the crew leaving the ship.

In practice the assembly of the ship will not be the
easy matter our description might convey. Before making any decisions the designers will subject every possible alternative to mathematical analysis, and examine
them from every point of view. We have only explained
the general principles of such a ship in the light of
present day experience.

Now the space ship is ready to be used for the purpose
we have mentioned. It now has to be equipped with
everything necessary for the lives and scientific work of
the crew. We must not forget the apparatus for regen-
erating air, supplies of food, the helio electric plant for
heating and lighting, the radar, the supply of rockets
and the space suits for leaving the ship, the scientific
instruments and the cinema equipment—another great
problem.

And now come the final preparations. The rocket motor is firing well. The passengers are already in the
narrow cabin . . . The ship is putting on speed. Ten
minutes have elapsed since the launching and the exhausts fall silent. The ship is moving along an ellipse
which will take it beyond the moon's orbit. The captain
switches on the apparatus to ventilate the empty tanks,
removing the last vestiges of fuel and making it fit for
habitation. This operation will take more than an hour.
At last, the captain opens the door of the cabin which
from now on is a living room and laboratory combined.

The instruments which could have been damaged by the fuel are now installed in the tanks. The crew settle down to their prescribed jobs . . .

But now the moon is approaching. By means of his small lateral rockets the captain turns his craft with the nozzles to the fore; the motors roar once more and the moon has a manned satellite. Now the front tanks can be jettisoned, having performed their task. This is accomplished "the peaceful way," by disconnecting the electro magnet which held them in place. But the rockets seem unwilling to leave the motor ship and fly on behind it. To shake them off a member of the crew will fire an ordinary signal rocket at them. After this impetus they will start to lag behind and will finally disappear in space.

On completion of its program of lunar observation the motors are switched on again and the reverse route is taken . . . A few days and the earth is once more within reach. The crew retire once more to their cabin taking with them the most precious instruments. A slight jolt and the lower part—everything except the wings and the nose—becomes detached, and disappears into the darkness. No longer guided and unadapted to fly through the atmosphere it will burn up on contact with the air. A few burnt fragments may perhaps reach the ground.

The captain takes his glider carefully down into the atmosphere, regulating the wings and the speed of his immersion; the wings brake his speed. The skin of his glider heats and cools alternately as he repeats the immersions and feels his way down. The excellent heat resisting quality of the cabin has safeguarded the crew from abrupt changes of atmosphere but the air inside becomes so hot that it is difficult to breathe. This maneuver lasts for several hours. Finally the glider enters the denser air and glides down to its base.

The World Next to Ours

Most people I am sure have read H. G. Wells's *The First Men in the Moon.* The explorers in this novel have a series of adventures among the Selenites—the dwellers on the moon who resemble huge intelligent ants. They have transformed the moon into a gigantic anthill by excavating grottoes, galleries and underground passages.

This novel was written nearly 50 years ago. At the time this brilliant author did not possess our present day knowledge of the physical nature of the earth's satellite and thus considered it to be habitable.

What is the modern view? Will the first astronauts to land there find the moon inhabited?

In any manual of astronomy will be found a detailed map of the moon's surface, photographs of certain regions and a description of its strange contours. A host of details will be seen on these maps of the moon: its surface has been explored through telescopes far better than many regions of the earth. The temperature at its surface has been accurately measured, revealing traces of atmosphere with a density of 1/2000th of the earth's atmosphere. It is difficult in earth conditions to reproduce such a rarefied gas.

The Moon is a dead world according to all descriptions. The day and night last 29.53 earth days, one lunar day being half a terrestrial month. The Sun's rays, meeting no atmosphric buffer beat down remorselessly, giving the surface a temperature of between 100° and 120°. In the friable dust of the moon you could cook an egg, roast a joint or make a fine vegetable soup. . . .

At night, again with no atmospheric buffer, the surface cools to about 160° below. This is a cold that has never been observed on earth in natural conditions.

Temperatures of this nature on earth can only be produced artificially with costly and complicated refrigerators. At such temperatures the basic gases which form our atmosphere would liquefy. The differences in temperature between day and night on the moon amount to 280°.

Nothing similar has been seen on earth. By comparison, a decidedly hot region like the Sahara is only a weak reflection of the moon. In the atmosphere above the vast expanse of the Sahara there is no water vapor to have a mitigating influence, no watercourses to collect the water, and the sandy soil heats and cools rapidly. The differences in heat between day and night are high, reaching 50°. By day travellers stifle in the intense heat and cannot drink at night because the water freezes in their leather skins. But this difference in temperature cannot be compared with that of the Moon. Moreover the terrible heat of day on the moon's surface is relative. In K. Ziolkowsky's amazing work of science fiction, *On The Moon,* the explorers go to ground and take cover in a deep crevasse. This would perhaps be unnecessary; the shade of some rock would be a natural refrigerator. If the travellers were to place two bottles of water on the moon's surface a yard and a half apart, one in the sun and one in the shade, the former would explode and the second would turn to ice.

The highest temperatures recorded on the moon do not penetrate below the surface of that planet; in all probability at a depth of a few inches the difference in temperature would not exeed 10° while at a depth of about 3 ft. it would remain constant. Instead of the atmospheric cover which protects the earth from excessive high and low temperatures, there is a layer of fine porous dust, the particles of which barely touch, through which heat can only percolate by radiation.

This absence of air and water and the unfavorable temperature conditions lead us to believe that there is no life on the moon. Nevertheless it is not the dead, motionless, immutable world it appears.

There is a great deal we do not yet know about this neighbor of ours. There are many mysteries on its surface and it has posed many riddles and problems to our astrophysicists and astronomers. When the telescope first discovered the mountains of the moon, the polar snows of Mars and the dense layers of cloud shrouding Venus, observers were struck by the similarity that exists between all the planets of our solar system.

Today we are more aware of the differences that exist between them. In fact we find very few formations similar to the earth on the surface of the planets we study through our telescopes.

Characteristic of the moon's surface, are the huge "circusses," and the mountain chains which seem to have been drawn with a ruler. What are they? The marks left by falling meteorites, or by gas bubbles rising from the interior of the planet and bursting on its surface? We know of nothing similar either on earth or on the other planets.

In the southern hemisphere of the moon is located one of the best known and most beautiful of the moon craters—Ticho. From it in all directions spread bright lines like the meridians of a pole. The length of these lines is many thousand miles, and they are to be found in a number of other craters. We can give no explanation for the formation of these lines. They are the monopoly of our nocturnal companion.

On the rocky southern shores of the Sea of Rains is a comparatively small crater—Eratosthenes. Hardly has the sun's rays illuminated its depths than it emits curious light rays. In the center appears a large stain which constantly increases in size. Towards the middle of the lunar day it reaches its maximum before starting to decrease. It gives the impression of an immense cloud of insects rising from the depths of the moon and following the solar rays.

Soviet scientists have definitely established that these patches could not be formed by the shadow of invisible objects. A member of the Russian Academy of Science, N. Barabasciov explains this phenomenon as the appearance and evaporation of rime which alternately hides and reveals the darker surface of the planet. Another explanation is equally plausible. The bottom of the Eratosthenes crater consists of rocks which undergo certain modifications from natural causes. Only our astronauts will finally discover the secret of these dark patches which are to be found in Eratosthenes and in other craters on the moon.

Many other strange phenomena have been observed by astronomers. The final explanations may turn out to be very unexpected . . .

Such is the moon, our next door neighbor, so well known as one might say on first sight; the first world on which our new space men will set foot.

The Lunar City

A space ship of curious design—we already know the appearance of our composite rocket—churning up the dust on the moon's surface with its flaming exhausts has landed heavily on its broad tripod. It rocked for a moment—one of the feet had landed in a crevice—but righted itself; the foot had automatically lengthened to rest securely on the bottom of the crevice. The dust thrown up by the exhausts, settled almost immediately and immobility returned to this dead world whose peace had been disturbed by the landing of our space ship. . . .

It would appear as though this ant-like contraption with the tripod legs descending from the round tanks would become a part of the silent landscape. But the unexpected visitors are restless spirits from the earth. Now they have set foot on this dusty surface it will never again know peace.

A port opens silently in the ship's side (due to the lack of atmosphere the moon is an almost silent world!) and a frail ladder is lowered. A man climbs down it in a suit of transparent plastic material which makes him look like a diver. His face is youthful and his keen, attentive eyes gleam with excitement.

And there is cause for excitement: to this man goes the honor of being the first to set foot on another planet. Impatiently he leaps down from 18 to 25 feet and lands very gently—*a la lune*. He is followed by a second and a third passenger . . .

They form a circle and a light aluminum pole is stuck in to the soil of the moon. A flag is hoisted; it does not flutter because there is no wind. Tears of emotion sting the eyes of the pioneers.

The first steps of the first men in the moon!

The initial refuge of these space travellers will be the space ship itself. But the cabins are narrow and uncomfortable. They have been designed to the requirements of the payload. New apparatus will be sent to them in pilotless rockets. It will have to be assembled as a permanent construction.

Armed with a geologist's hammer, making leaps of about 20 yards at a time, one of the crew makes for the nearest rocks. What will the Moon offer to its first inhabitants? Will it offer nothing but stone covered with fine dust, fiery hot by day and ice cold by night?

No, the moon may be far mre hospitable. In the foothills of the nearest mountain they will find caves of all shapes and sizes. Their corridors will lead into gigantic chambers or narrow into fissures. Here is their first haven.

The astronauts will shoulder a number of cases—on earth they would take 5 men to lift—and make for the hidden caves. In the most suitable they will build their first lunar house.

They are carrying their house on their backs. Now the floor of the cave is already covered with a thin sheet of plastic. One of the astronauts affixes a kind of armadillo's shell which at the back has a window instead of a door. This will be the front door of their house, a double door which will serve for their incomings and outgoings. These doors will only open in succession—the second as soon as the first has been closed. If they opened simultaneously the warm air would leave the house and mix with the rarefied atmosphere of the moon.

In the meantime, a second member of the party has secured to the valves of the unrolled sheet tubes connected to the oxygen tanks. The house starts to inflate like a balloon.

Now it stands in the cave, illuminated by the space men's electric torches.

The building is circular like an eskimo's igloo; it has a diameter of 24 ft. and is about 9 ft. high. After opening the door with a key, taking great care not to let the air out, the astronauts enter their house with their necessary equipment. The first house on the moon!

Everything here, of course, is "for the first time" and borders upon the marvellous. Once inside they are in no hurry to shed their space suits; it must first be warmed. In this cave the cold is appalling—in the region of 100° below. The sun's rays never penetrate it. When the electric heaters are installed they notice how slowly the liquids which will not freeze at 15° below zero rise in the tubes. The temperature continues to rise . . . Now they can remove their space suits.

Helping each other they remove their transparent helmets and the diver's suits which have been impeding their free movement. Finally they can stretch out to each other a friendly hand no longer encased in a double layer of rubber.

The appointments of the first house are Spartan in

the extreme. They consist in the main of apparatuses to purify the air. The pressure is revealing—only 30½ lower than on earth at sea level. Although the oxygen content of this air is higher than on earth it does not inconvenience the newcomers. During the whole flight they have breathed the same mixture. The use of such a mixture allows the total amount of air brought from the earth to be reduced a little.

Secondly, there are the heaters and the accumulators to feed them and produce light. Heat must be economized. The accumulators will not last long. Although the double plastic wall is a weak conductor of heat, the escape will be reduced. The moon possesses an unlimited quantity of insulating matter—the dust which covers the surface. After a brief rest they put on their space suits once more and go out. Their house is already covered with the dust which settles everywhere on the moon's surface. This insulating dust has already formed a complete hill outside the door.

Their habitation is now ready on general lines. In their lair the astronauts need not fear meteorites. Later, having investigated its air tightness, after taking a few precautions such as covering it with mastic or special paint, after hermetically sealing the slightest cracks and fissures except one, they will have succeeded in transforming the whole cave into a habitation. This will be most advantageous for they will be able to make a host of observations while remaining in this heated and lighted cave, filled with air brought from the earth.

And at last the first sound is heard on the moon.

Now the first lunar house is not so badly appointed as might appear at first sight. There are soft seats and

chests of the same plastic material, hammocks and
tables. All these were an integrated part of the balloon
when it is inflated.

There are no windows, but they are unnecessary. The
astronauts, by this time thoroughly exhausted, lie down
in their hammocks.

They will not calculate time by lunar days but by
earth days from the lunar dawn. In the 20 hours since
the rocket landed, the sun has hardly risen in the sky.
The second day will also be devoted to work. The first
transport rocket will arrive: it lands about a mile from
where the astronauts landed but fortunately a little
nearer to their new house. After unloading this rocket
they will have a further provision of oxygen, a small
caterpillar wheeled with an airtight cabin, transparent
plastic bonnet and its own fuel. The pilotless rockets
will now arrive without interruption. The earth will
not leave these pioneers to their own resources.

The second rocket carries the helio-electric plant. This
is indispensable. The accumulators will already be fairly
well charged during the flight, little energy having been
expended for heating, lighting and the radio apparatus.

The astronauts will start to assemble the helio-electric station in an open, sunny spot. It will not differ
from the model used in the space ship. A special clock-
work device turns its long, narrow concave mirror towards the sun. Beneath the vaults of the cave, electric
lamps will now be burning.

This helio-electric station will work at full blast, uninterruptedly. The accumulators will have to be sufficiently charged during the lunar day to last the whole
of the lunar night. The astronauts will dismantle the

ship in which they will eventually return to earth and with the aid of the special truck take it piecemeal to the cave. They will do this as a precaution against meteorites. On the unprotected surface of the moon will remain only the helio-electric plant, the wireless aerials, the radio-telescope and the temporary observatory installed in one of the empty fuel tanks. The second tank is in the cave. It will serve as a fuel container. In case of emergency this could be used for domestic purposes.

This is how we imagine the first house on the moon today. Obviously we have not foreseen everything and perhaps some of our guesses may be wrong. Time alone will tell. But one thing is absolutely certain: this reconnaissance flight to the moon will undoubtedly take place. The earth will send its messengers everything they need for life and for their scientific work. Each day the tracks of their car will venture a little farther from their cave. Ever larger tracts will be surveyed. A lunar city will rise. New arrivals will relieve the pioneers who will work only for a determined period. They will adapt other cover for living quarters, stores and work. Eventually everything will not have to be sent up from the earth. The resources of the Moon will be discovered. Perhaps layers of fossilized ice which will provide not only water but the oxygen they need to breathe will be found. Water can be transformed into oxygen and hydrogen by means of the electric current. Greenhouses will be built on the moon and fruits will be grown. Perhaps metal deposits of sulphur and other minerals will be found.

In time the first industrial city will be founded with a spacedrome, a scientific center and a transit station for longer interplanetary journeys.

It will not be founded until long after the first plastic

house has been re-transported to earth to be put on display in a museum next to Popov's thunderbolts and Stephenson's "rocket."

When Will It Happen?

The "discovery of the Moon" will not take place today or tomorrow. Only in science fiction does the brilliant inventor of a space ship leave for the Moon, Mars or even more distant planets. In reality, the problems of inter-planetary travel are so grandiose that their solution will not be the work of a single man but of a whole team of brilliant scientists.

Only their combined work will allow these problems to be solved. The concerted efforts of thousands of men is needed and this requires a great deal of time. The whole venture can only be realized very slowly.

The Soviet physicist, V. V. Dobronravov has analyzed the development time of modern technicology; in view of the importance of space travel he has given some indication of the time he considers will be needed for this great task. According to him, the solution will probably be divided into three stages:

The first stage is the creation of pilotless rockets capable of rising to a height of 200-250 miles until an artificial earth satellite has been created. This marvellous stage has been reached by our Sputnik.

The second stage is man's penetration into space. First the flight of specially constructed manned rockets, then the inhabited satellite, and finally the creation of a space station—an outpost on the way to the stars. This stage will conclude with the flight of a manned ship to the moon. 1980 is the date he forecasts for this.

The third and final stage envisages visits to the moon and the other nearby planets of our solar system with landings. The date of such flights to the Moon with return to earth Dobronravov forecasts as the year 2,000. These dates must be considered on the pessimistic side. Despite the complexity of the problems involved, we are of the opinion that it will be very much in advance of that given by the learned professor.

Chapter Eight

JOURNEYS TO OUTER SPACE

In Search of Life on Other Planets

AS soon as the atomic rocket has been perfected, flights to the Moon, Mars and Venus with landings on those planets will no longer be costly and complicated undertakings. These flights will only be possible by leaving from an artificial satellite—the space station. To realize them the assembly of these heavy, cumbersome ship will be carried out in space under difficult conditions; they will probably be multiple staged rockets. However, everything is possible to modern science. Plans for visiting the nearest planets of our solar system already exist.

One of these plans presupposes the assembly of the space fleet on the satellite. Three-stepped "freighters" (according to some calculations they might be in ten sections) will deliver to the circular orbit the necessary amount of fuel, components and instruments of the ships destined to make the journey. A fleet of 10 gigantic ships each weighing 3,720 tons will be equipped for the job.

They will be Leviathans, externally quite different from those rockets whose parts have been despatched from earth to build the artificial satellite. They will be composed of separate spherical tanks of real or synthetic rubber. Their solidity will not have to be very great since they will only have the resistance of inertia to overcome.

At the opportune moment the motors will be switched on, the fleet will leave the circular for a hyperbolic trajectory which will then become elliptical at a tangent to the orbit of Mars. The motors of each ship will be in action for more than an hour and their thrust will not be more than 200 tons. During this hour most of the fuel will have been burnt and the subsequent weight of each ship will then be only 906 tons.

The flight will last 260 days and at the end of this time the fleet will be approaching the red planet Mars. The motors will be switched on again to bring the ships onto the circular orbit of Mars. Now the weight will have been reduced to 410 tons.

At last the moment will come for the landing on the planet. Three landing craft, provided with broad wings will be used for the glide down through the rarified atmosphere of Mars. The payload carried will amount to about 150 tons. This will consist of transport equipment, pneumatic crates, scientific apparatus—everything in fact needed by a scientific expedition of 50 men for a period of more than 400 days.

As a start one of these craft will land on the polar region of the planet. The landing will probably be on skids. This ship will remain forever on Mars so that the 125 tons of fuel necessary for relaunching it will carry equipment, jeeps, etc. Its crew will start exploring the surface of Mars further south for a suitable landing place for their two companions; these will still have enough fuel in their tanks for the return journey and a payload of 12 tons. These two ships will land on wheeled undercarriages.

Mars is smaller than the earth, its gravitational pull is smaller and the circular velocity of a body which has become a satellite is a little more than 2.6 miles per second. Thus a launching from Mars is easily possible with single stage rocket.

Having left the spare equipment on Mars, dismantled the wings and undercarriage essential for landing but not for takeoff, stowed the specimens and samples collected in the cabins, the whole expedition will foregather in the passenger cabins of the two ships which have landed near the equator. The motors will roar once more with their thrust of 200 tons.

Each ship will burn about 110 tons of fuel to reach circular orbit and several more tons to coordinate its movements with that of the seven ships left behind in the circular orbit. The three ships which have finally rejoined the pack will remain in the satellite orbit of Mars.

Now all the members of the expedition will take their places in the cabins. The weight of each ship is now 408 tons including the 222 tons of fuel needed for the return journey to the earth satellite.

This is the plan devised by Wernher von Braun for a space expedition to Mars. It has been carefully worked out to the last detail from the engineering point of view;

it would seem to be practicable in the light of modern techniques. According to von Braun the major obstacle to its realization is the astronomical cost of the expedition. The essential expenses are high because of the need to deliver to the artificial satellite the initial load of the expedition—some 37,200 tons consisting of the ships and their fuel.

To launch this load, thousands of three stepped rockets will have to be sent up consuming 5,580 tons of fuel each journey. The total consumption will amount to 5,580 tons, and the cost of this fuel will be the principal expense of the expedition. The balance of the cost of the flight from the earth satellite to Mars and return will amount to barely 1.1½ of the cost of the fuel.

These figures apply of course to a fleet running on liquid propellant: but the position may change rapidly if atomic motors are perfected. In the sections previously allocated to fuel could be carried a sufficient quantity of fissionable matter to suffice the launching from earth, landing on a nearby planet and return to earth. During the journey there would be no need to worry about running out of fuel.

The expedition from Earth will leave relatively soon for the nearest planets. The first to be visited will probably be Mars.

Mars the mysterious world . . . our neighbor in the solar system and bearing a great resemblance to us. The ruby red planet which since time immemorial has given rise to legends.

Mars is considerably smaller than the earth: its diameter is only 4210 miles and its mass is 0.1 of the earth's mass. It describes its orbit at a speed of 3.05 miles/s at a mean distance from the sun one and a half times that of the Earth. Mars completes this rotation in 686.98 days and a rotation on its own axis in 27 hrs. 37' 23.6". The inclination of its axis is almost parallel to the earth's and in consequence its seasons resemble our own. For this reason it has often been called the earth's twin.

Mars is enveloped by an atmosphere considerably more rarefied and of a different chemical composition. It contains far less oxygen. This atmosphere is full of clouds which rain solid rime: mists swirl around it morning and evening.

The poles of Mars are covered with white caps which vary in size according to the season, increasing in winter and decreasing in summer. It would appear that these polar regions are subject to the same laws as apply on earth: In the spring the ice recedes towards the poles; in autumn and winter it creeps down towards the equator. Intensive study has shown that the white Martian caps definitely have a covering of ice.

But this does not end the similarity between the twin planets. The surface of Mars shows no important expanses of water. From pole to pole it is a solid, smooth and uniform surface. No noticeable mountain ranges, rocks or hills. The entire contours of Mars consist of dunes, sandy curling dunes formed by the winds.

The climate is harsher than ours. In winter the temperature at sea level is from −50° to −80°. In the equatorial belt it rises at midday to 25°, but descends at night to well below zero. In the polar regions during the long summer days it remains constant between zero and 15°.

The smooth reddish surface of Mars has a series of dark clearly defined patches. These are usually called "seas," but they are, in all probability, regions of damp soil covered with vegetation.

Their coloring changes according to the season. For most of the year the patches in the equatorial region are sky blue, grey and greenish grey. From spring to autumn some of them have a misty green appearance.

The seas and gulfs in the temperate zone are only blue and green in the summer. The nearer the dark patches approach the pole the shorter the period of their coloring. By autumn they have changed to brown.

All this is curiously reminiscent of our earth's vegetation. But how can we prove that life exists on Mars— even if only in vegetable form? How can we convince ourselves that the messengers from earth will not only meet with an inert chaos of rocks, solid granite masses and poisonous tempests of methane?

A reply to these questions has been given by the Soviet scientist, Gabriel Tihov, a member of the Soviet Academy of Science.

Tihov sets out to prove that the dark changing patches on Mars are belts of vegetation. To this end he cites the properties of their terrestrial counterpart.

Photographers know that if on a sunny day they take a shot of a pine or a fir through an infra red filter the foliage will come out white on the print as though covered with snow. Most plants reflect infra red in toto, and this is why such photographs can be obtained.

The Soviet scholar examined photographs of Mars cutting out the infra red rays. His reasoning was as follows: If the seas and gulfs do not show white it proves that they are regions covered with vegetation like those on earth. But if there are no white patches on the photos taken the "seas" of Mars do not reflect infra red rays.

Tihov turned to studying the properties of the plants on earth. He discovered that only plants living in warm climates reflected infra red rays well; they receive so much warmth from the sun that they have no need of the infra-red heat and reflect it.

Arctic plants, however, behave quite differently: the firs and mosses in the cold regions of the earth, deprived of the sun's heat, in order to keep up their vitality are forced to absorb both the visible and infra red rays. On photos taken with infra red filters they do not turn white as the seas of Mars also failed to do.

We have already mentioned that Mars is farther away from the Sun than the Earth, making its climate similar to that found in our polar regions. The plant life on Mars should therefore be very similar to our arctic flora.

Thus the experiment which seemed to have failed became a convincing proof of the existence of vegetable life on that planet. "Probably," Thihov writes, "evergreens of the type of our mosses and stunted plants with hard leaves like our myrtles thrive on Mars. There may also be aspens not unlike our dwarf birches."

Today research as to whether plant life exists on other planets as well as Mars has created a new branch of science: astrobotany. In the Soviet Academy of Science a new branch has been created for this study: it has achieved praiseworthy results under Gabriel Tihov.

His students have discovered new facts which have confirmed and enlarged our knowledge of life on other planets. We can safely state that the Earth is not the only bearer of life in our solar system and that the future space travellers will undoubtedly find vegetation on Mars.

The time will come when special hothouses are built

on Earth in which conditions reigning on Mars will be artificially reproduced and seeds brought from that planet will be cultivated. Perhaps some of them will be found capable of adapting themselves to certain arctic conditions here below. Who knows whether they will not have properties of extraordinary advantage to man?

Does a fauna—or animals, birds, insects and reasoning beings exist on Mars?

It is almost impossible to answer this question. But it is probable that the development of the organic world has not stopped at vegetable forms of life: certain animal organisms will undoubtedly have evolved.

While we are on this subject, it is necessary to refer to another phenomenon to be observed on Mars: the canals.

The canals of Mars: these geometrical lines which extend from one of the seas were discovered by the Italian astronomer Angelo Secchi about 100 years ago, in 1859.[1] He christened them with this unfortunate name which has given rise to so much controversy but which has fortunately increased the interest shown in Mars by the public as well as by astronomers.

The existence of canals was confirmed by another Italian astronomer, Giovanni Schiaparelli. He was struck by the geometrical precision of these lines which intersected in various directions on the reddish Martian deserts. Schiaparelli discovered that they had other peculiarities: they never crossed half way, but issued from

[1] Credit for discovering the "canals" of Mars is given to G. Schiaparelli, not to Secchi. (Ref. Ency. Brit.) Discovery was made during an exceptionally favorable opposition of the two planets in 1877, and Schiaparelli called the wispy lines he saw "canali," which in translation means "channels" or "grooves," not "canals."

the seas and rejoined them. Wherever the canals met could be observed a small patch.

In 1893, Schiaparelli published an article in which he propounded the theory that the Martian canals had been built by being capable of reasoning;[2] that they had been distributed across the planet to catch the meagre reserves of water from the melting snows and the polar ice and that there were large stretches of fields and gardens cultivated by the industrious population of this planet along the canals.

Today it seems more probable that the canals are stretches of vegetation. Their changes of color are identical with those found on the vegetation of the Martian seas. Furthermore these changes do not occur haphazardly, but start from the polar caps in spring as though water from the melting ice ran along their beds at a rate of 2-4 m.p.h. and in consequence fructified the plants. But the discussion still continues. In September 1956, occurred the "great opposition of Mars." The two planets had approached to the nearest point on their orbits: they were now only 35,000,000 miles apart. Telescopes of all sizes all over the world were focussed on the red planet. Astronomical observations are still inadequate but astronauts will soon be in a position to solve this ticklish problem. In our opinion the canals are fractures in the soil of Mars and we do not subscribe to the view that they were built by beings capable of reasoning. And yet why should not the other theory be true? Why should

[2] In the hands of the American Percival Lowell, these canali became canals and he told of the intelligent life on Mars that had built them. (Ref., "Our Neighbour Worlds," V. A. Firsoff, Philosophical Library, N. Y., 1953, p. 240.)

the Earth have the sole prerogative of being the bearer of intelligence in our solar system?

This question usually receives the following answer: if the Martians were capable of such a vast engineering feat why have they not yet landed on the Earth?

But why have we not yet flown to Mars? We who have created huge artificial seas all over our planet? Our engineering feats are no less than those of the Martians in concept, if we take into consideration the short span of our building period and the reduced gravitational pull on Mars which is only 0.38 of the earth's. Let us recall the magnificent and perfect systems of irrigation built by the peoples of antiquity in Egypt, Assyria and China. These systems were built when man had not conceived the idea of interplanetary flight. Perhaps today the development of Martian technology, too, is on the threshold of a voyage of discovery to the Earth just as ours is plannig a trip to Mars.

Nevertheless the astronauts who fly for the first time to this planet, which undoubtedly possesses life, will have to foresee the possibility of meeting inhabitants of a level of culture and development by no way inferior to our own . . .

The Planets of which We Know Nothing

Do such planets, then, exist in the solar system?

Hardly has the Sun risen above the horizon at dawn, than we can see an extraordinarily beautiful star which reflects a bluish white light. It bears the name of the Goddess of Beauty—Venus. Its other names in antiquity were the Morning and Evening Star.

Astronomers have naturally measured and weighed this planet. It is nearer to the earth than Mars by 10 million miles. Venus's orbit round the Sun is within that of the earth. Its linear diameter is hardly smaller than ours, measuring 7,600 miles and it is surrounded by a thick layer of atmosphere which was discovered in 1761 by M. Lomonosov.

The astrophysicists can give some further information on this atmosphere to future astronauts. They maintain that it is opaque and that the latter will glide through dense clouds of steam which hide the view of this beautiful planet like a veil. From the length of its dusk we can calculate the weight of this atmosphere as three or four times greater than that of the earth. The temperature of the upper layers of the clouds on Venus is known to us: it is about 50° on the illuminated and −23° on the dark side. We have no definitive data on its chemical constitution. It would seem that the upper layers contain a large quantity of carbon dioxide and nitrogen but little oxygen.

As we have already said, Venus is far nearer to the Sun than the Earth. The Aurora Borealis which quivers in the upper atmosphere above the Earth's poles are caused by the penetration of streams of corpuscles from the Sun.

A number of these particles also fall on Venus. The intensity of her Aurora Borealis must exceed ours. This has recently been confirmed by observation.

Let us ask the astronomers and astrophysicists to tell us the structure of the surface of Venus and what physical conditions the future astronauts will find. Could it be covered with a boundless ocean in ebullience from which from time to time volcanoes erupt in a cascade of flame and smoke? Is it a sandy desert lashed by winds which throw up clouds of dust to hamper the view or a jungle of luxuriant red and orange vegetation? Palms with broad carmine leaves, stout cherry red licuras and a blood-red soil? What is its temperature and how long is its day? There are no answers to these simple questions.

How can we say that man has discovered Venus, the beautiful Star of the Morning which the ancient shepherds of Babel admired? Will man ever be able to learn as much about her as he already knows of the Moon and Mars? Probably not.

Improvements in the known methods of research such as spectrum analyses may give the answer to some of the questions, as for example the composition of the atmosphere of Venus. The increased power of radar is a very accurate way of exploring, because its rays will be able to give us some idea of her contours and continents. But only the astronauts in their space ship will really be able to discover Venus.

The first flights to this planet will certainly be exploratory and without landings. On nearing the mysterious planet the captain will change the trajectory of his ship making it an artificial satellite of this planet which does not possess one. At close quarters and applying the latest infra red methods the astronauts from their observatory in space will be able to see through the dense layer of clouds and check the composition, structure, weight and atmospheric density, and the nature of its surface; and make the necessary survey for a future landing.

Not until this has been done will the conquest of this planet materialize. If the space ship by its power and structure can possibly land it will do so. Then another world after the Moon and Mars will join the number of those visited by man.

The landing on Venus will in all probability have to be postponed until after a succession of exploratory flights: after calculating his reserves of fuel the captain will see that they are insufficient for a launching from the planet and a return to earth.

On the other hand it is in the cards that a visit to this planet will never materialize: if for example it consists of a boundless ocean without a patch of terra firma. Then the only advanced outposts of science will be the artificial satellites which will undoubtedly be sent up to this planet.

There is no doubt that Venus too will be opened up in this way for the good of science and the human race.

Mercury is even nearer to the Sun than Venus. It revolves so near to it in fact that it is almost melted by its rays. Copernicus tried all his life to see this planet but never succeeded.

Mercury is considerably smaller than the earth and not much larger than the Moon. Its diameter is 3,000 miles and its year is equal to 88 earth days. Like the Moon it revolves with its face constantly turned to the Sun.

The atmosphere of Mercury is hardly denser than that of the Moon and there is a great similarity between these two worlds. During the day it has no protection afforded by an atmosphere and its surface reaches a temperature of 410°. At this heat lead and tin melt. It can be assumed that the sun's rays illuminating this planet are reflected from glittering lakes of these liquid metals.

The other face of Mercury is the realm of eternal night, lit only by the stars and the other planets, and a

cold which certainly differs little from that of outer
space. On one side, then, lakes of molten metal and on
the other frozen rocks and solidified nitrogen and ovygen.

Between these two contrasting regions a narrow stretch
must exist with a climate which would allow a landing
to be made.

It would obviously be on this strip that the astronauts would try and land their ship and set out on a
voyage of exploration.

By its ratio of reverberation the surface of Mercury
resembles that of the Moon. Its surface like the Moon's
—at least on the side lit by the sun—is also unequal,
porous and rugged with high relief: there are no mountain ranges.

Towards the Sun

A flight to Mercury, owing to its proximity to the
sun, will only be possible in a ship furnished with a
special protective skin against solar radiation.

In interplanetary space the best means of communicating heat from one body to another is by radiation. It
is a popular fallacy that only incandescent bodies emit
rays. All heated bodies generate some kind of rays, the
degree of radiation depending upon the heat of the
particular body.

Everyone knows how a very hot object can burn even
though it is not red hot, as for example the door of a
stove. It is generally believed that the air is heated by
the metal and that we feel the heat of this air: this is
untrue. We are feeling the heat of the infra-red rays
radiated by the metal object.

If we heat the object to about 600° we shall notice that it gives off a cherry red glow. Heated still further it becomes a vivid red and then white. Each change of color corresponds to a given temperature of the object.

The reason why the heat does not burn the faces of the workers making steel at 1000° is because they wear a dark glass visor which does not allow the infra red rays to pass. The bright helmets of firemen serve the same purpose: they are made bright to let them reflect the maximum amount of rays.

As a defense against solar radiation, the space ship of the future on its way to our nearest planet to the sun, will be protected from its rays by a series of spaced shields. With the protection of these "sunshades" it will be able to complete the major part of its voyage.

The exterior and largest screen will be in the most unfavorable conditions. Although its smooth surface will reflect the major part of the deadly rays the temperature will rise to an inadmissible degree. The melting or softening point of this metal must be considered. This shield will have to be given intensive cooling. By a system of hollow tubes a liquid coolant will be circulated exactly on the principles of a motor car. The cooling radiators for this liquid will be the natural refrigerators on the dark side of the same screen in space. This cooling process will also take place by radiation.

The second shield will receive on its exterior only the radiation from the outer shield; it will be entirely in the shade. It may be necessary to add a third. In the shade of these three shields the space ship will be able to approach within a relatively short distance of the Sun.

How would the members of the expedition be able to study the planet unless protected by similar shields?

Appertures could be pierced in the shields through which a narrow beam, without deflection and not weakened by a layer of atmosphere, could be allowed to fall into the laboratory to give all the data it could about the sun. Secondly, special filters could be used to absorb all except a very narrow strip of the spectrum. And, finally, the same shields could be made to allow only a certain part of the spectrum to pass through them. Then the astronaut would be face to face with the mighty sun, with its black spots and the flames spurting from its disc.

Will this be necessary on such a flight?

Most certainly. Not merely scientific interests or an attempt at a sensational record, but purely practical reasons will determine this.

Solar energy is the cause and the base of all life on earth and on the other planets. Solar energy is the wind which drives the sails of the windmill and the water which functions the blades of hydroelectric power stations. Solar energy is contained in the lumps of coal we burn in our furnaces, in the drops of heavy naphtha whose explosions drive internal combustion engines: and the sun keeps our planet at a temperature at which it is possible to live in the atmosphere on terra firma and in the depths of the sea.

Why should man not approach the sun and examine its mechanism as far as possible?

Time on earth is dependent upon solar radiation. It is the solar activity which determines the intensity of the Aurora Borealis and the magnetic storms. Radio transmissions and the future radio communications with the space ship are largely dependent upon solar activity.

Who knows whether in the future man will not be able to influence the prime source of factors as important as time in the atmosphere and "space time"?

The sun is a gigantic laboratory in which at temperatures, pressures, degrees of ionization and other conditions unavailable, mysterious reacitons in substances and complicated physical processes are brought about. One of the lightest gases, helium, was first discovered on the sun; it serves to inflate balloons and airships. Perhaps these mysterious processes can be examined near the sun and be copied on earth to the advantage of the human race. No, man must not renounce this undertaking. Sooner or later this flight will be made because human curiosity is unlimited and there are no secrets which nature will not ultimately reveal.

Among the Planets and their Satellites

It is difficult to prognosticate, but flights to the Moon, Venus, Mars and Mercury will have been made within ten or twenty years and perhaps may take place at any moment. The geophysical year has seen the launching of the first two Sputniks and the launching of a manned rocket.[3] It is certain that eventually man will add other planets to the number of those conquered.

From Mars outward this will mean the next in order from the Sun, Jupiter. Space is far from safe for interplanetary travel. If we compare meteorites with submarine rocks which face the mariner—incidentally a very

[3] The X-2 rocket ship went to 126,000 feet altitude and returned safely with pilot, but that was before the IGY.

much greater danger—on these long journeys through space there will be a greater chance of meeting such unwelcome visitors.

In an American science fiction story, astronauts of the future find an asteroid of gold and bring it back to earth. It is highly unlikely that a gold asteroid will ever be brought back from space but some made of this precious metal may actually exist. On the other hand they represent a very grave danger to space ships. From the earth we can only observe the larger asteroids, miniature plants of some scores of miles in diameter. Some which have been plotted are even smaller than this. But it is difficult to foresee how many fragments weighing a few grams or a few thousand tons may be roving about in space. It is probable that they are legion and if they were to hit a space ship they would utterly destroy it.

In the future a space weather service will be created; it will take into account all the arrant meteorites, streams of asteroids and give the least dangerous routes to be followed. Later we may see spcial measures taken to free the space routes from these "dangers to shipping." But this will be in the far distant future. At the outset the asteroid ring will be a considerable obstacle for space ships on their way to the remoter planets.

Another obstacle in the conquest of the ultra-Martian planets will be distance and the length of flight. A flight to Jupiter and return on an elliptical orbit would take 6 years. The trip to Saturn would take 12 and to Uranus 30 whole years! Space travellers would have to spend the best part of their lives in the narrow cabin of a rocket!

The use of atomic power would partly overcome this obstacle. With its aid the ship could leave the ellipse, avoid passing through the asteroid belt and be either above or below it. Atomic energy, too, would allow the ship to develop a velocity that would reduce the duration of flight to the furthermost planets, Neptune and Pluto, from decades to perhaps months and weeks.

Landing on these planets would not come under consideration for a very long time. According to the astronomers they are composed mainly of gas: Jupiter and Saturn of oxygen, Uranus and Neptune of ammonia, methane and water. The solid core of all these planets is at great depth, far below the strata where pressure reaches a degree that will transform the gases into compressed liquid. A space ship subjected to the gravitational pull of Jupiter would sink into its atmosphere and be destroyed by the titanic gas pressure, just as water pressure will burst a hermetically sealed bottle at the bottom of the sea, as soon as it had penetrated a tenth of the potent atmosphere of this huge planet.

But a flight to the ultra-Martian planets will be of the greatest interest. Let us take an imaginary flight in the finest space ship that has ever been built. In it we should be able to land on any planet or its satellite and to overcome the incredible distances. Let us try and figure out what the travellers who may one day undertake one of these journeys would see on the way.

The orbit of Mars has been left behind and ahead of us lies the mysterious asteroid belt. These miniature planets have the greatest variety of closed and elongated orbits. Some, as they near the sun, penetrate the orbit of Mercury, while others are attracted by Jupiter.

Let us brake the speed of our ship near one of these asteroids. A huge mass moves along its own orbit, slowly rotating and offering all its faces to the rays of the sun.

It is very irregular in shape. It could not have an atmosphere, except for a short time, its force of attraction being too small. There could be no life on its surface.

The theory has been put forward that in the future once artificial suns have been created at various points in the solar system, when, according to Ziolkowsky, man will have "conquered all the space around the sun," these tiny planets will be used by space architects as building material. This is not impossible. These rocks which have flown for centuries through space, are made of the same minerals as the rocks on earth. Without doubt the future space architects will find that they contain precious metals—iron and nickel in its pure state which could be used for the floors of the space greenhouses. Maybe they will obtain appreciable quantities of gold from some of these asteroids. Even gold could find a practical use in this space world where every lb. of material sent up from the earth is worth its weight in gold.

A further suggestion to use the asteroids to the good of humanity has been put forward. This refers to the asteroids with elongated trajectories like Icarus. They will be used as "ocean going ships" which could carry sloops, canoes and other light craft on long voyages. Thus, anchored to the captive asteroid a space ship could undertake journeys of considerable length. In certain cases the space trip on an asteroid would offer more room than a simple trip in a man built ship. According to A. Sternfeld, at the end of these "transoceanic voyages" special "orbital ships" would be built which would move round the sun on extensive trajectories chosen to give convenient interplanetary communication. Anchored to this type of "Transatlantic liner" the space ship on passing near the earth's orbit would fly for example as far as the orbit of Jupiter. But let us continue with our journey.

The sun's rays now illuminate alternately large and small asteroids which rotate slowly on their own axis; their twinkle constantly changes. Pursuing their own orbits they move away from us rapidly and are soon no more than trembling stars which disappear into the darkness with a final twinkle. . . .

Once more we are forging ahead at full speed. Ahead of us in the velvety black night looms the largest of our planets: Jupiter. We can clearly distinguish its white polar caps and its golden tints with dark lines round the equator. It rotates at a great speed on its own axis: a day on this huge planet lasts only 10 hours.

Jupiter is about five times removed from the sun in comparison with the Earth. Thus it completes its circumsolar orbit slower than the earth. A year on Jupiter corresponds to 12 earth years.

In its majestic passage round the sun the giant planet is accompanied by a troop of 12 gleaming satellites. Twelve moons the size of our own familiar Moon, if not larger, like a small family of asteroids. Their diameters vary from between 10-60 miles. Indubitably man will one day set foot on all these icy satellites. Astronauts will erect on them observatories to watch the movements of the solar system. What is the nature of the dark stripes round the equator of Jupiter? What causes the tints of its cloudy atmosphere to change alternately from red to yellow? How can we explain the temperature which is 15° higher than it should be with reference to solar radiations? Is this due to volcanic activity, to the fission of radioactive elements or to the production of heat under great pressure? And finally what does it hide beneath the monstrous envelope of its atmosphere? Does a layer of ice 15,000 miles deep surround a metal core as the astronomer Wildt believes, or does hydrogen, a component of the planet under colossal gas pressure at a depth of 6,500 miles below the visible surface become solidified as A. Massevich believes?

How many mysteries will this golden balloon, which sails so slowly through the sky, reveal to the astronauts by the light of its lucent moons?

We push on ahead: our ship makes a gigantic bound. Jupiter is left far behind and to starboard suddenly emerges the most beautiful of all the planets: Saturn with its unique ring.

This ring is so large that our world placed on it would look like a cherry in a lady's large straw hat. The magnificent golden disc of the planet seems like some fabulous jewel created by a magic jeweler against a black background of sky.

But our ship could not descend on this planet. As in the case of Jupiter we do not know the composition of its surface. Saturn is probably a sphere of icy gas like Jupiter. The upper atmosphere has a temperature of $-155°$, $15°$ lower than that of Jupiter. Many gases liquefy and freeze at this point.

Now our ship approaches the colossal planet which has a diameter of 75,100 miles. We can already distinguish the structure of its surface: dark and light stripes, color spots which appear and disappear in its atmosphere. As on Jupiter, storms and hurricanes rage in this ocean of gas in the process of congealing which conceals the mysterious core of this planet.

Of Saturn's nine moons the sixth is the most interesting—Titan. It is nearly twice the size of our Moon and is covered with an atmosphere of methane. The physical nature of this satellite will therefore have to be studied from afar. Putting on speed we approach the ring of Saturn. Their weight is insignificant compared with their breadth which is between 10 and 15 miles. It consists of an almost solid stream of meteorites flattened like a leaf; some of these reach a size of 30-45 ft. Their facets, covered with white rime, glitter in the sun. Our ship puts on speed once more. To reach the orbit of the next known planet, Uranus, we have to cover twice the distance already covered. The mean distance of Uranus from the Sun is 1,880,000,000 miles. Its orbit is nearly the same from the earth. To cover this distance a shell fired from a fantastic cannon flying at a speed of 1.5 miles/s would need 45 years to reach it. The space journey to Uranus following an elliptical trajectory would take more than 16 years. Press on!

Uranus . . . despite its vast dimension this huge planet with a diameter of 30,900 miles is difficult to see with the naked eye because it is so far from the earth. For half their journey the astronauts from earth will only see it through their ports as a tiny star. But now we are approaching the monster. The disc appears to have a greenish tinge.

It is even colder on Uranus than on Saturn. Its surface temperature is −170°. Powerful telescopes can distinguish on its disc stripes of the same type as are to be seen on Jupiter and Saturn.

The sequence of the days, nights and seasons on Uranus are complicated and of great interest. As the result of a cosmic catastrophe or obeying some law, of which we are still ignorant, of the whole solar system,

Uranus is on a very inclined axis: its rotary axis is almost exactly horizontal to the plane of its orbit. Thanks to this position Uranus offers its poles to the sun one after the other. Its year equals 84 earth years. A day at one pole lasts 42 years while the other pole is in total darkness. On all the intermediate latitudes, about every 21 years, day and night are equal, but on one hemisphere the days draw out and on the other the nights. Then at a latitude 35°, on one hemisphere the day lasts 21 years while in the other hemisphere at the same latitude it is night; then begins a period of 21 years when the days and nights are equal. Then as though the hemispheres had changed position the whole performance is repeated in reverse.

Uranus has 5 satellites. The plane of their orbits is almost perpendicular to the orbit of the planet.

Now we must travel even further . . . Neptune the next planet in the solar system is 2,810,000,000 miles from the sun. Our burning sun which cannot be looked at with the naked eye except through smoked glass looks from here like a bright star, its disc barely distinguishable.

Now we are approaching the confines of our solar system as we know it. It only remains to visit Pluto, a planet discovered only a few years ago, in 1930. Pluto is comparatively near Neptune and thanks to its very elongated orbit it is sometimes nearer to the Sun than Neptune. This world is so far from the sun and lit so weakly by its rays that it has not yet been measured. It is computed to be larger than Mars and smaller than the earth. Its orbit round the sun takes 248.5 years.

Our ship descends a little towards its surface which consists of solidified gas transformed into ice: oxygen, nitrogen and methane. Above this celestial desert, above all the rocks in which the stars are reflected, rises a bright yellow star whose disc is hardly visible—our Sun. It is now 40 times further away than from the Earth. Its rays are powerless to dispel the darkness of this world. A twilight like a white northern night is its calm daylight. We turn our backs on our own sun as it rises above the horizon and the shadow of our ship like the dark line of a road runs towards the horizon. We are at the confines of our solar system and can stare out into the infinite space ahead of us. We have travelled millions and millions of miles in our imagination in a true space ship. These boundless distances within our system are immeasurable compared with the distances which separate our Sun from the other nearest suns. And now we are looking out on an infinite, inconceivable ocean. Is this the definite barrier which nature has placed on man's path and which, despite all his audacity, he will never be able to cross?

Towards the Stars

We, the inhabitants of the northern hemisphere, only see the stars nearest to our solar system.

It is a modest insignificant star which is obviously ignored by the inhabitants of the southern hemisphere who can admire the spectacular Southern Cross. Astronomers know that this small star is only 4 light years away. It is called Proxima and its rays travelling at the speed of light reach us in 4 years, 3 months and 7 days.

All the other stars are much further away from our solar system: between two, three, a hundred, a thousand, a million times further. To reach Proxima in Centauri in a space ship equipped to reach the confines of our system, would take 60,000 years. How many generations would live inside that cabin until the travellers, instead of a star could see ahead of them the disc of this new sun?

So flights to the stars are impossible?

The fatal word "impossible" has often played tricks on timid men who have no faith in the power of their intellects.

"Flight in heavier than air machines is impossible," they said when the first aeroplanes were planned.

"Flight to the moon and to the other planets of our solar system is impossible," was the current opinion fifty years ago.

Let us look back in time. What today is taken as a matter of course would have appeared impossible 150 years ago. Electric light, registration of sound, photography, reproduction on the television screen, radio transmission and telephotography, motor cars, tractors, artificial silk, steam turbines, hydraulic turbines, electric motors etc. . . . All these were impossible! And all these have been invented since 1810, less than 150 years ago!

In the days of Pushkin the tale of a man who possessed a camera would have been related to the science fiction shelves. The description of a televisor would have been found fantastic. Not even wireless waves had yet been discovered, the basis of television. The discoverer, Hertz was born 20 years after Pushkin's death in 1857.

As a general rule the most audacious theories based on confidence in the human brain and in its powers turn out to be practical.

In the 13th century lived the famous English philosopher, Roger Bacon. Here are the words of his marvelous prophecy on the potentialities of science. They were written in 1267:

"It is possible to build navigating craft which function without oars, a fluvial and marine vessel guided by a single man faster than if it were rowed by many. It would also be possible to build coaches with horses to travel at an undreamed of speed . . . Flying machines could be built in which man would use wings like the birds. A machine could be planned to circulate without danger at the bottom of the sea and the rivers. . . . Transparent objects could be constructed in such a way that distant objects would appear close at hand, so that the smallest letters and the minutest objects could be distinguished at incredible distances as clearly as we see the stars, the sun and the moon from the earth. . . ."

At that time none of the ideas seemed credible. And now ideas even more impossible than these have been realized.

Convinced that no barriers or limits of knowledge exist we might say that the unknown exists but it is not unknowable. No, the boundless ocean of interstellar space will not stop man. In his stubbornness he will set out to explore these far off suns. Naturally this will not happen in our time nor for many generations.

The day will come when an ultra speedy space ship will approach the shadowy regions of Proxima in Centauri. It will be the largest space ship ever to have appeared in the skies. It will run on entirely new principles. The exhausts will not emit gas but fragments of disintegrated nuclei. The power of this primordial substance will permit speeds approaching the speed of light.

The passengers will not be subjected to the strain of acceleration. The acceleration of 30 ft. per second will offset gravitational pull and they will feel as little in the cabin as if they were sitting in a chair by the fireside at home. After 123 days, when the speed of the rocket will have reached 60,000 miles an hour the motors will be disconnected. At this moment the sun will have become a small distant star in space and the earth will have disappeared from view.

The ship will fly on its momentum. The astronaut's time will be occupied in scientific work, observations and research. Naturally the 12 years will not pass without leaving their traces:[4] but it is certain that by that time human life will already have been considerably prolonged.

The small almost invisible star, Proxima, will become the brightest star in the firmament. They will have to start braking, radiating before them columns of the substance launched at the speed of light and slowing down their speed to the required rate. After 123 days, the captain will be able to land his ship on one of Proxima's planets.

We shall not attempt to guess what we shall find there; whether the unknown planet will offer a refrigerator, the burning heat of a desert or the air of polar ice. Our description of a space ship for interplanetary travel is as vague as Bacon's was of an aeroplane in the 13th century. This is of no importance. The universe has no limits. But neither have the powers of the human brain and the audacity of man.

[4] Some mention is warranted here about Einstein's "time dilation" theory, which in broad terms says that time slows down as speed increases. This phenomenon is not apparent until the speed approaches that of light.

Chapter Nine

CONCLUSION

THIS book is essentially a book of the future since the practical application of space travel in all its vast conception belongs to the future.

But the future is indissolubly bound up with the present and its roots are founded in the present. One only has to look, to see clearly the first seeds which will be the flowering plants of tomorrow.

These seeds are the conquests of many branches of science: astronomy, physics, thermo-chemistry medicine, radio, technicology, metallurgy etc. . . .

The solution of all the problems inherent in space travel will demand the concentration, knowledge and experience of many branches of science.

The successes to date are the jet engines of supersonic aircraft, liquid and solid propellant rockets, radar control and a host of other achievements. The designers of the future space ships will be able to call upon all this wealth for their future work.

But what will count more will be the enthusiasts in-
tent upon solving the problems of space travel who will
work in this field with a generous expenditure of energy,
time, knowledge and experience.

Until recently only a few enthusiasts such as Ziolkowsky, Sander and Kondratiuk bothered their heads with
this subject. Today astronautical societies exist in every
country. In countries like the U.S.A., France and Great
Britain they have acquired thousands of adherents. Astronautical congresses are held where scientists impart
the results of their work and discuss plans for the
future. The Soviet Union also possesses a Society of
Astronauts. Four years ago the first meeting of the
Astronautical Section took place in the Central Aeroclub.
In the vast brightly lit hall of the House of Aviation on
whose walls were displayed many models of aircraft from
"flying birdcages" to the supersonic jets, the space travel
enthusiasts foregathered, scientists, engineers, doctors
and university students. The purpose of the meeting was
to plan the realization of space travel. The Astronautical
Section has today a series of scientific and technological
committees to work out the various problems involved.

Doctors and biologists from the biological committee
study the effects of space travel on the human body and
are founding the new cosmic medicine.

The astronomers forecast the conditions which man
will meet on his way to other planets. Their task is to
find safe routes for the space ships—routes where they
will not be bombarded with meteorites, and the methods of defense against this menace.

The rocket engineers are faced with a whole range
of difficult problems: the building of rocket motors and
space ships for long interplanetary journeys, methods

of cooling the walls of the combustion chambers and nozzles and finding heat resisting materials. These are subjects for many lectures to be given by the special faculty for astronautics in the university.

The work of the committee for space communications plays an important role in the general scheme: they have to work out the best ways of reaching another planet, to calculate the trajectories, to determine the hours for launching and landing and to find methods of orientation in space.

The specialists of automation and tele-mechanics, students and engineers work on the radar control of space ships. Some of them study schemes for a super-powerful radar capable of accompanying the ship as far as Mars; thus the most exciting branches of modern science, radar and automation have been enrolled in the service of space travel.

The work of the technological committee consists in studying the problem as a whole. Space clubs attached to the Moscow Section exist in many of the cities of the USSR and in many of the institutes for advanced studies.

The work in the field of astronautics is on a national scale. A co-ordinating committee has been founded in the Soviet Academy of Science to direct the activities of the various institutes. The president of this committee is the academician, L. I. Sedov.

The Academy awards a special medal called the "Ziolkowsky medal" for outstanding achievements in the field of astronautics.

In the USSR a review called Interplanetary Communications has just been published. Space communications are of colossal importance. It is impossible to exaggerate their significance for the development of science and the progress of the human race. The consequences which the solution of these problems may have are only comparable with the discovery of atomic energy. Nevertheless for the present this problem is fraught with great difficulties. Each step forward demands strenuous work and concentration of the intellect use and productive forces of races.

There is no doubt that the contributions of scientists, engineers and enthusiasts from all over the world, including our own, have already given and will continue to give great support to the astronautical world. In the coming years this work will reap its own reward. Today we have taken the first step with the Sputnik, our artificial satellite. This has been followed by a second step—the launching of a man miles into space with a safe return.[1]

In the old days, men lived in a restricted society and many of them never stirred from their own villages. Today that age seems grotesque. How is it possible that men did not know the earth was round, that the continent of America existed and that the world could be circumnavigated? Today every elementary schoolboy knows that the earth revolves round the sun, turns on its own axis and that the stars are only distant suns, similar to our own.

The time will come when today's knowledge and the successes of which we are so proud will appear insignificant to our descendants, who are destined to win a hold over nature such as only science fiction writers dare to suggest today.

We should not envy the ancient prophets who struggled for truth. It deeply concerns us. The men of the

[1] No confirmation of this is now known in this country.

Age of discovery—Columbus, Vasco di Gama and Magellan had the good fortune to open up the terrestrial globe. Galileo, Bruno, Copernicus and their followers managed to define the position of the earth in space.

In our day there is still room for great discoveries. Our generation has been called to be the first to set its foot on the neighboring planets.

Nor must we envy the men of the future for whom many things which appear fantastic to us will be a commonplace.

We have been privileged to make the first step: and it is for the men of the future to envy us our happiness.